Tom Adams, Steve Langfield, Claire Hutchinson and [

C000018441

Exam Practice Workbook

OCR Gateway
GCSE Science B

Contents

1. The table below provides information about blood pressure.

	Systolic (mm Hg)	Diastolic (mm Hg)
Normal blood pressure	Below 120	Below 80
High blood pressure	Above 140	Above 120

Jim is 28. He works in an office and has been promoted to a more responsible job. He works long hours and tends to relax by going to the pub with his mates after work. He had a cold a few months ago but apart from this he is free from infection.

(a) Jim is given a blood pressure meter to monitor his blood pressure on a daily basis. He records his readings as shown.

Day	Monday	Tuesday	Wednesday	Thursday
Blood pressure	142/92	139/89	144/93	142/90

Calculate Jim's average **diastolic** blood pressure. Show your working. [2]

92 + 89 + 93 + 90 = 364 ÷ 4 = 91 _____ mm Hg

(b) Jim goes to see the doctor about his blood pressure. Suggest **two** pieces of advice his doctor is likely to give him. [2]

* One advice the docter might give him is to reduce the intake of alcohol and sugar.

(c) Jim decides to get fitter and starts running with his friend Bob. Bob is a regular runner. They fit heart rate monitors to themselves and after exercise Bob finds his heart rate returns to a resting level of 80 bpm within four minutes. Write down how you would expect Jim's monitor information to be different. [2]

Jim's monitor information because his resting rate would be higher.

(d) Bob says Jim is healthy but not fit. Do you agree with Bob? Explain why. [2]

Yes, I agree with Bob because Jim is healthy-free from infection, but is not as capable as doing as much physical activity as Bob.

2. **(a)** Study the diagram of the artery below. Arteries can become blocked when fatty deposits build up in them. A heart attack results when a component of the blood blocks the vessel at **X**. Name this component. _Thrombus_ [1]

[Total: ____ /9]

Higher Tier

(b) Explain how this leads to a heart attack. In your answer you should include the name of the vessel which becomes blocked and ideas about cardiac muscle and its requirements. [3]

Vessel blocked _~~Arteries veins~~ Coronary artery_

Explanation _Oxygen can not go to the heart. muscle Therefore oxygen will not be able to pump around the body which will cause the heart to stop._

3. Carbon monoxide can prevent blood from carrying enough oxygen. Explain how. [2]

Carbon monoxide can prevent blood from carrying oxygen because it will decrease the amount of carbon dioxide

4. It is important to have a blood pressure as this allows blood to be pumped through the various which vessels and reach all tissues of the body. When blood pressure is too high however, this can helps lead to problems. respire.

(a) Describe **two** problems that can be caused by high blood pressure. [2]

(b) Describe **one** consequence of having low blood pressure. [1]

[Total: ____ / 8]

(margin handwriting): the able to go to the heart be will not able to respire. oxygen will not be able to the heart muscle Therefore muscle will die and end

1. Karen is determined to improve her lifestyle and make it more healthy. Here is a list of food groups she needs to include for a balanced diet.

   carbohydrates   protein   fats   vitamins   minerals

   (a) Ring two food groups she should cut down on to reduce her energy intake.   [1]

   (b) Complete the following sentence.   [1]

   Vitamin C is important for a healthy diet because

   ....

   (c) A genetic screening shows that Karen might be susceptible to bowel cancer. Write down **one** food group she should **increase** in order to lower her risk.   [1]

   ....

2. The table below provides a guideline for the recommended Body Mass Index.

BMI	What it means
<18.5	Underweight – too light for your height
18.5–25	Ideal – correct weight range for your height
25–30	Overweight – too heavy for your height
30–40	Obese – much too heavy, health risks!

   (a) Karen is 1.54 m tall and weighs 66 kg.

   The formula for calculating BMI is:

   $$BMI = \frac{mass\ (kg)}{height\ (m)^2}$$

   Use this to calculate Karen's BMI to the nearest whole number. Show your working.   [2]

   ....

   (b) Describe what this BMI means for Karen.   [1]

   ....

3. (a) Elouise eats 35g of protein per day. She weighs 63kg. Use the equation below to decide whether Elouise is getting enough protein in her diet.   [3]

   EAR (in g) = 0.6 × body mass (in kg)

   ....

(b) Elouise is aged 16. Explain why it is especially important for teenagers to have enough protein in their diet. [1]

....

[Total: .... / 10]

Higher Tier

(c) Elouise is a vegetarian. Which phrase describes the type of protein Elouise will eat? Choose from the list.

  1st class protein   2nd class protein   3rd class protein   [1]

4.   The table below shows how obesity in 2–10 year-old children has changed between the years 1995–2003 in the UK.

Year	% of obese children in UK
1995	9.9
1996	10.2
1997	10.8
1998	11.3
1999	11.8
2000	12.3
2001	12.8
2002	13.3
2003	13.7

(a) Predict the percentage obesity for 2004 based on this trend. ....[1]

(b) If the body's daily energy requirements are exceeded, sugar can be converted to storage products, for example fat under the skin. Name **one other** storage product and where it would be found. [2]

....

[Total: .... / 4]

1. Draw lines to link the name of the microorganism to the disease or condition it causes. [3]

Bacteria		Flu
Fungi		Malaria
Viruses		Cholera
Protozoa		Athlete's foot

2. Dakoba is a region in Africa where mosquitoes breed rapidly and malaria is very common. Harriet is a British student visiting the region. She notices mosquitoes landing on the skin of babies and sucking their blood. When e-mailing her parents she tells them that parasitic mosquitoes are attacking the babies.

(a) Explain why she is wrong to describe the mosquitoes as parasites. [2]

....

....

(b) Next day, Harriet cuts herself on a dirty stick while making a fire. How will the white blood cells **around the wound** respond? [1]

....

(c) Despite this, some of the bacteria survive and multiply in the wound. Describe how they will harm Harriet's body. [1]

....

3. New drugs have to be carefully tested to check that they are effective and safe. Two methods are animal testing and computer modelling. Give **one advantage** and **one disadvantage** of each type of test. [4]

Drug testing method	Advantage	Disadvantage
Animal testing		
Computer modelling		

4. Rani has caught flu and has been confined to bed for several days. Her mother is a health worker and was immunised against flu in the previous month.

   (a) Describe how the different types of blood components will deal with the viruses in Rani's body.

   (i) White blood cells (Phagocytes) .... [1]

   ....

   (ii) Antibodies .... [1]

   ....

   [Total: .... / 13]

Higher Tier

   (b) Describe how the cells in Rani's mother's body responded to the vaccination she was given. In your answer state what was in the vaccine and use the words **antigen, antibody** and **memory cells**. [4]

   ....

   ....

   ....

   ....

   (c) After four days Rani is still unwell and she is taken to the doctor. The doctor advises plenty of rest, regular intake of fluids and painkillers when necessary. Explain why he does not prescribe antibiotics. [2]

   ....

   ....

5. What is meant by a **double blind trial**? [2]

   ....

   ....

   [Total: .... / 8]

1. Finish labelling the diagram of the motor neurone below. [2]

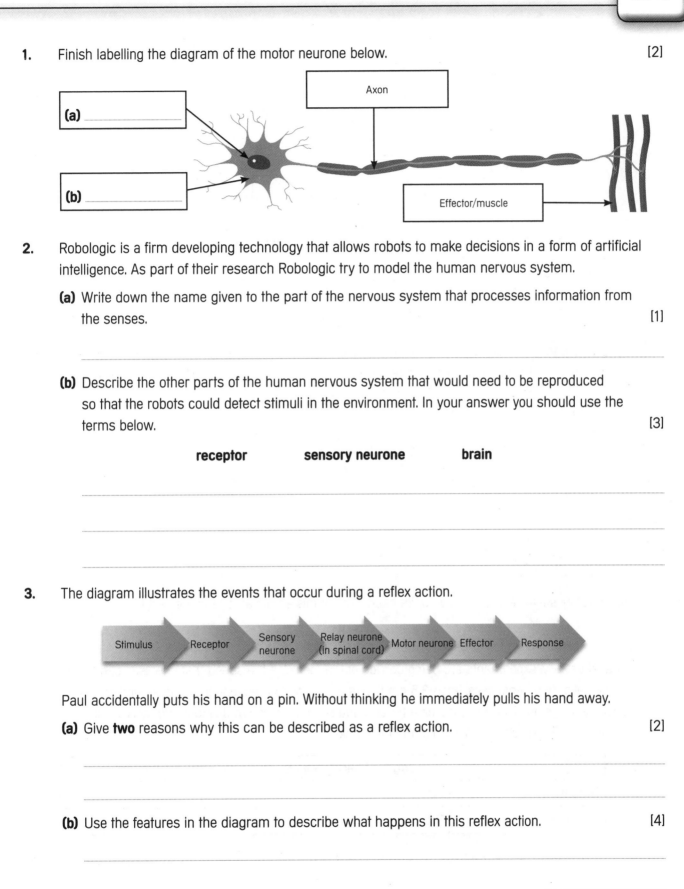

(a) ....

Axon

(b) ....

Effector/muscle

2. Robologic is a firm developing technology that allows robots to make decisions in a form of artificial intelligence. As part of their research Robologic try to model the human nervous system.

(a) Write down the name given to the part of the nervous system that processes information from the senses. [1]

....

(b) Describe the other parts of the human nervous system that would need to be reproduced so that the robots could detect stimuli in the environment. In your answer you should use the terms below. [3]

receptor   **sensory neurone**   **brain**

....

....

....

3. The diagram illustrates the events that occur during a reflex action.

Stimulus → Receptor → Sensory neurone → Relay neurone (in spinal cord) → Motor neurone → Effector → Response

Paul accidentally puts his hand on a pin. Without thinking he immediately pulls his hand away.

(a) Give **two** reasons why this can be described as a reflex action. [2]

....

....

(b) Use the features in the diagram to describe what happens in this reflex action. [4]

....

....

....

....

....

4. The eye is an example of a sense organ.

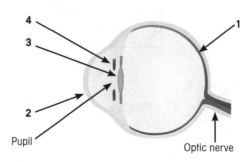

(a) Match **A**, **B**, **C** and **D** with labels **1–4** on the diagram. Enter the numbers in the correct boxes below.

A Lens ◯   **B** Retina ◯

C Cornea ◯   **D** Iris ◯   [4]

(b) The diagram below shows the eye focusing on a distant object. Describe what happens to the light in order for it to be focused on the retina. In your answer, name the parts of the eye involved.   [2]

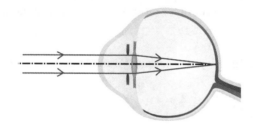

....

....

(c) A rabbit's eyes are at the side of its head. Why is this an advantage to the rabbit?   [1]

....

5. In a laboratory, experiments are being carried out to measure the speed that impulses can travel down nerve cells. Two nerve cells, each 3.5 cm in length, are compared, one in a human and one in a cockroach. Using electrodes, the time for an impulse to travel down this length of nerve cell is measured. The results are shown in the table below.

	Length of nerve cell/cm	Time for impulse/s
Human	3.5	0.0015
Cockroach	3.5	0.0019

Which animal do you think has faster responses? Use evidence from the table to explain your answer. [2]

....

[Total: .... / 21]

6. The diagram below shows a junction between two nerve cells.

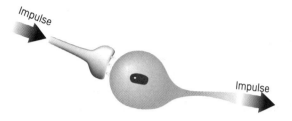

Impulse

Impulse

(a) What name is given to this nerve junction? .... [1]

(b) The nerve cell receiving the impulse is a **motor neurone**. Describe the adaptations of this neurone to the job it does. [3]

Elongated shape ....

Fatty sheath ....

Branched endings ....

(c) In order for the impulse to be transmitted from one neurone to the next, a **transmitter substance** needs to be released. Describe the sequence of events involved. [3]

....

....

....

[Total: .... / 7]

1. Complete the table below in order to name the group of drugs which each example belongs to.
   The first one has been done for you. Choose from: [4]

   sedative   **stimulant**   **depressant**   **painkiller**   **hallucinogen**

LSD	hallucinogen
Nicotine	
Alcohol	
Paracetamol	
Tamazepam	

2. **(a)** UK law classifies drugs according to an A, B, C system. Write down **two** ways in which a class A drug would differ from a class C drug. [2]

   ....

   ....

   (b) John has been addicted to heroin for three years now. What does the word **addicted** mean? [1]

   ....

   (c) As John continues to take heroin, he finds he is becoming more **tolerant** to it. Explain what this means. [2]

   ....

   ....

   (d) Under advice, John is admitted to a rehabilitation centre. While 'coming off' heroin he experiences **withdrawal symptoms**. Name **two** symptoms he might experience. [2]

   .... **and** ....

3. The table shows how smoking can affect a person's chances of getting lung cancer.

Number of cigarettes smoked per day	Increased chance of lung cancer compared to non-smokers
5	4 ×
10	8 ×
15	12 ×
20	16 ×

(a) Estimate the increased chance of lung cancer if someone smoked 25 cigarettes per day. [1]

....

(b) Describe and explain how smoking heavily can cause emphysema. [2]

....

....

....

(c) Apart from lung cancer and emphysema, name **one other** disease that can be caused by smoking cigarettes.

[1]

....

[Total: .... / 15]

Higher Tier

4. **Stimulants** and **depressants** both have an effect on nerve junctions. Explain how each behaves. You may use diagrams to help your explanation. [4]

....

....

....

....

....

....

....

[Total: .... / 4]

1. Rafiq is enjoying a skiing holiday but not the cold! His body works to keep at a constant temperature.

   (a) Name the process which governs how conditions are kept constant in the body. [1]

   ....

   (b) List **two other** conditions which need to be kept constant in the body. [2]

   .... **and** ....

   (c) After standing around waiting for a ski lift, Rafiq starts to shiver. Explain how this helps him to conserve heat. [2]

   ....

   ....

   ....

   (d) After skiing cross-country for a while, Rafiq starts to sweat underneath his thermals. Explain how sweating enables him to lose heat. [2]

   ....

   ....

   ....

   (e) Rafiq's internal body temperature has changed very little during the day. What temperature is this likely to be? Ring the correct answer. [1]

           30°C   **35°C**   **37°C**   **40°C**   **50°C**

   (f) Explain why this temperature needs to be maintained. [1]

   ....

2. Label the gland shown on the diagram and add the name of a hormone it produces. [2]

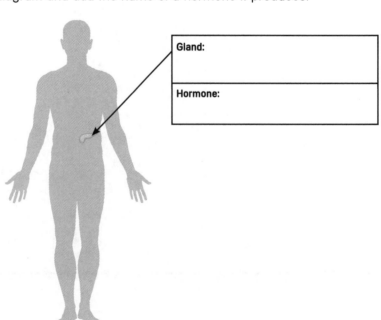

Gland:
Hormone:

3. Nanotechnology is a rapidly advancing area of research and makes use of tiny artificial structures down to a molecular level. A new nanotechnology device has been developed for people with diabetes that can detect levels of glucose in the blood and communicate this information to a hormone implant elsewhere in the body. The implant releases a precise quantity of hormone into the bloodstream when required.

(a) Explain how this device could help a person with type 1 diabetes who has just eaten a meal.   [2]

....

....

(b) Explain why a person with type 2 diabetes might not have as much use for this technology.   [1]

....

4. Study the graph.

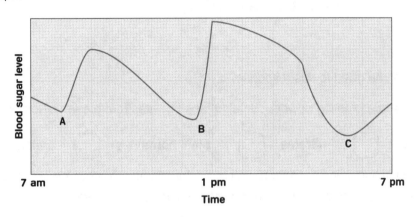

(a) How can we tell from the graph that this person has diabetes?   [2]

....

(b) Explain why the person's blood sugar level rises rapidly just after points **A** and **B**.   [1]

....

(c) What would have happened after points **A** and **B** if the person did not have diabetes?   [1]

....

(d) Why did the person need to eat a chocolate bar at point **C**?   [1]

....

[Total: .... / 19]

B1 Controlling Plant Growth

1. This question is about plant growth.

(a) Name **two** factors which plants are sensitive to. [2]

.... **and** ....

(b) Miriam is carrying out an investigation into the germination of a broad bean seed. The diagram shows the appearance of a seed she planted after five days. Label the shoot and the root on the diagram. [2]

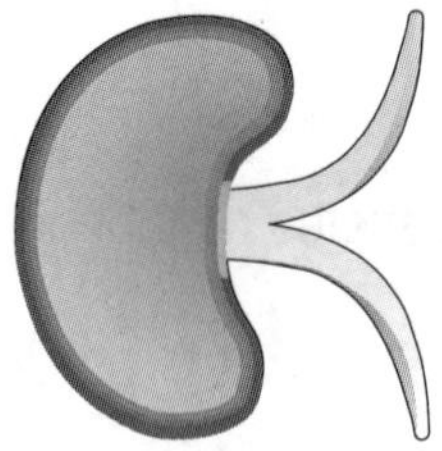

(c) Describe how the shoot has responded to gravity. [1]

....

(d) What is the name given to this response? .... [1]

2. Which substance does rooting powder contain that stimulates root growth? Tick (✓) the correct box.

enzymes ☐ **nitrates** ☐ **plant hormones** ☐ **vitamins** ☐ [1]

3. In another investigation, Miriam wants to find out if the shoots will grow towards the light. Describe an experiment she could do to show this. Your answer should have two sections:

- a method
- the likely results she would get.

✏ *The quality of your written communication will be assessed in this question.* [6]

....

....

....

....

....

....

....

....

....

....

[Total: .... / 13]

1. Draw lines between the boxes to connect each term with the correct definition. [3]

Nucleus	Different forms of the same gene
Chromosomes	Cell structure that contains the chromosomes
Genes	Consist of large numbers of genes
Alleles	Small pieces of DNA that control the development of a characteristic

2. Next to each type of human cell, write down the number of chromosomes it would contain. [3]

Red blood cell _____   **Sperm cell** _____

Skin cell _____   **Ovum** _____

3. **(a)** George is trying to describe himself. For each feature below, state whether it is caused by **genetics**, the **environment** or a **combination** of both. [4]

(i) 2.01 m tall _____   **(ii)** Blue eyes _____

(iii) Blond hair _____   **(iv)** Scar on his forehead _____

(v) Speaks German _____   **(vi)** 120 kg weight _____

(b) George shares many features with his brother Nathan but he wants to know why he is not identical, even though they have the same parents. Explain to George why this should be so. Use ideas about fertilisation and gametes in your answer. [2]

_____

_____

_____

(c) George has a sister called Olwen. Describe how their sex chromosomes would be different. [1]

_____

(d) Olwen was born with a genetic condition called **cystic fibrosis**. George is worried that he might eventually catch this disease. Explain to him why he needn't worry. [2]

_____

_____

4. Mary is the owner of two dogs, both of which are about two years old. Both dogs are black in colour and came from the same litter of puppies.

(a) A dog's body cell has 78 chromosomes. How many chromosomes would be in a dog's sperm cells? [1]

_____

(b) The dogs' mother had white fur and the father had black fur. Use what you know about genes to explain how these parents could produce puppies with black fur. [2]

_____

_____

[Total: _____ / 18]

Higher Tier

(c) One year later, one of the black puppies mated with a white-haired dog. She had four puppies. Two had black fur and two had white fur. Draw a fully labelled genetic diagram to explain this. Using the letters **B** and **b** to represent the alleles for fur colour, show which offspring would be black and which would be white. [3]

5. Complete these two different crosses between a brown-eyed parent and a blue-eyed parent. [6]

(a) Brown eyes × Blue eyes

Parents (BB) × (bb)

Gametes ◯ ◯   ◯ ◯

Offspring ◯ ◯ ◯ ◯

▭ ▭ ▭ ▭

(b) Brown eyes × Blue eyes

Parents (Bb) × (bb)

Gametes ◯ ◯   ◯ ◯

Offspring ◯ ◯ ◯ ◯

▭ ▭ ▭ ▭

(c) Explain how parents who both have brown eyes could produce a child who has blue eyes. Use a genetic diagram to help you. [4]

6. **(a)** Janine has cystic fibrosis. Her mother and father did not show symptoms of the condition. Using 'c' as the allele for cystic fibrosis, draw a genetic diagram to show how this could occur. [4]

(b) What was the probability that Janine's parents would have produced a child with cystic fibrosis? [1]

(c) Which phrase describes the genotype of Janine's parents? Ring the correct answer.

homozygous dominant   **homozygous recessive**   **heterozygous** [1]

[Total: .... / 19]

1. Which of the following are types of invertebrates? Put a ring around the correct answers. **[3]**

    annelids   **reptiles**   **molluscs**   **crustaceans**   **fish**   **arachnids**

2. The picture shows a 'Liger'. It is the result of interbreeding between a lion and a tiger. The liger is infertile.

    (a) Explain why a lion and tiger are classed as separate species. **[1]**

    ....

    (b) Lions, tigers and leopards are all carnivorous big cats. They all have five toes on their front paws and four toes on their back paws. Their claws can be drawn back to avoid damage. They all roar. Tigers and leopards tend to be solitary animals but lions live in prides of females with one dominant male.

    (i) Underline one piece of evidence in the information above that suggests that lions, tigers and leopards are all descended from a common ancestor. **[1]**

    (ii) This table shows the binomial names of four species.

	Genus	Species
Lion	Panthera	leo
Tiger	Panthera	tigris
Leopard	Panthera	pardus
Snow leopard	Uncia	uncia

    Are leopards more closely related to tigers or snow leopards? Explain your answer. **[2]**

    ....

    ....

    ....

    [Total: .... / 7]

Higher Tier

3. Archaeopteryx is an ancient fossilised species of bird. When first discovered, scientists found it hard to classify. Bacteria are organisms which are also hard to classify but for different reasons.

 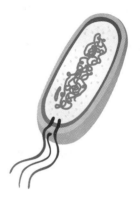

(a) Using features shown in the picture, explain why Archaeopteryx is difficult to classify. [2]

....

....

....

(b) If scientists wanted to determine if one species of bacterium was different from another, what difficulties would they face? [2]

....

....

....

(c) Explain how DNA sequencing might help scientists to classify bacteria. [2]

....

....

....

....

[Total: .... / 6]

B2 | Energy Flow

1. What is represented by the arrow on a food chain? Tick (✓) the correct answer. [1]

The main consumer ⬭   Transfer of energy ⬭

Loss of biomass ⬭   A pyramid ⬭

2. Apple trees are grown in orchards in temperate climates. They are part of a wider food web.

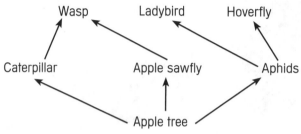

(a) The apple tree is a **producer**. What is meant by this term? [1]

....

(b) What is the source of energy for this food web? .... [1]

(c) Name a secondary consumer in the food web. .... [1]

(d) Below are two pyramids which describe the feeding levels in this food web. Which one accurately shows a **pyramid of biomass**? [1]

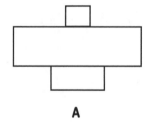   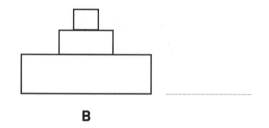

A   **B**

(e) Explain how energy can be lost between different feeding levels in the web. [2]

....

....

3. The picture shows the energy intake and use for a cow.

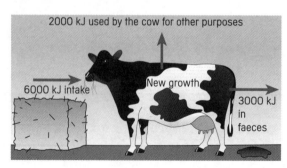

(a) Suggest what form the cow's energy intake is. .... [1]

(b) Suggest the **two** main types of energy that account for the 2000 kJ transferred in the cow. [1]

.... **and** ....

(c) Calculate the energy taken in by the cow which is used for new growth. [1]

....

[Total: .... / 10]

Higher Tier

4. **(a)** Using the formula below, calculate the energy efficiency for the cow. Show your working. [2]

$$\text{energy efficiency} = \frac{\text{energy used usefully for new growth}}{\text{energy taken in}} \times 100\%$$

....

(b) Humans do not need to eat as large a biomass as cows do. Explain why. [2]

....

....

(c) Use the information in answers **(a)** and **(b)** to explain why vegetarianism is more energy efficient than eating meat. In your answer, explain the implications for agricultural land use if significant numbers of a population are vegetarian. [6]

✎ *The quality of your written communication will be assessed in this question.*

....

....

....

....

....

....

....

....

....

[Total: .... / 10]

1. Carbon is an element found in all living things. It is recycled in the environment in a process called the **carbon cycle**. The main features of this cycle are shown below.

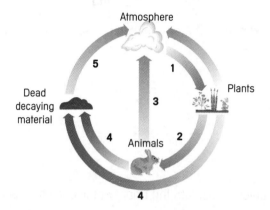

(a) Name the process which occurs at stage **3** in the diagram. _____ [1]

(b) The UK government is planning to use fewer fossil-fuel-burning power stations in the future. How might this affect the carbon cycle? Use ideas about **combustion** and **fossil fuel formation** in your answer. [2]

_____

_____

_____

2. Another important process in nature is the **nitrogen cycle.** The diagram below shows the main stages.

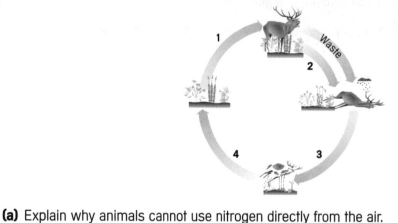

(a) Explain why animals cannot use nitrogen directly from the air. [1]

_____

(b) Match processes **A**, **B**, **C** and **D** with the labels **1–4** in the diagram. [2]

A Animals eat plants ◯

B Dead matter is broken down by decomposers ◯

C Plants absorb nitrates from soil ◯

D Death ◯

[Total: _____ / 6]

Higher Tier

3. Peat bogs are ancient habitats which can act as **carbon sinks**.

(a) Explain how a peat bog acts in this way. In your answer use ideas about the carbon cycle. [2]

....

....

....

(b) Carbon can also be locked inside limestone. Describe **two** ways in which this carbon can be released once more into the atmosphere. [2]

....

....

4. The diagram shows the roots of a pea plant.

(a) Name the type of bacteria that would be found in the root nodules. [1]

....

(b) Explain why these bacteria are important for the nitrogen cycle. [2]

....

....

(c) When animals die and decay, they are acted upon by decomposers. Complete the following equation which describes the decay process.

ammonium compounds $\xrightarrow{\text{nitrifying bacteria}}$ .... [1]

(d) Clover is also known to have root nodules. Explain why farmers might want to grow clover every third year in a field which normally contains wheat. [2]

....

....

[Total: .... / 10]

1. The size of a population of swallows found in the South of England was recorded every other summer from 1990.

   (a) Draw a graph of the data from the table. [3]

Year	No. of swallows
1990	956
1992	918
1994	876
1996	834
1998	797

   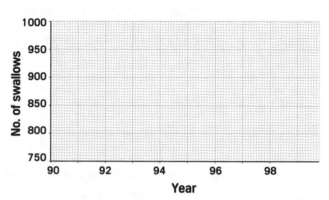

   (b) Estimate the size of the swallow population in the summer of 1999. [1]

   (c) In 1992, pesticides were introduced in the South of England which reduced the population of flying insects. Suggest how this might be connected with the decline in the number of swallows. [2]

2. The following information on the population of stoats and rabbits in a particular area was obtained over a period of ten years.

Year	1989	1990	1991	1992	1993	1994	1995	1996	1997	1998
No. of stoats	14	8	8	10	12	16	14	6	8	12
No. of rabbits	320	360	450	600	580	410	300	340	450	500

   (a) Plot these results onto the graph paper provided. [3]

   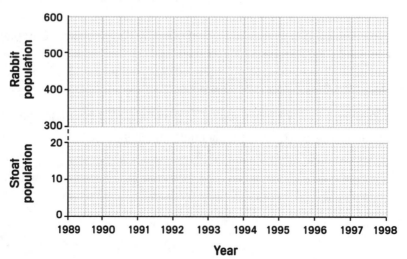

(b) Explain the reason for the variation in the size of the stoat and rabbit populations. [3]

....

....

....

[Total: .... / 12]

Higher Tier

3. **(a)** Leguminous plants (e.g. peas) have bacteria living in nodules on their roots. How do pea plants benefit from these colonies of nitrogen-fixing bacteria? [2]

....

....

....

....

(b) What do the bacteria gain from the relationship? [1]

....

....

4. Harlequin ladybirds have recently increased in number on the UK's south coast. They occupy the same ecological **niche** as the resident ladybirds.

(a) What is meant by **niche**? [1]

....

(b) The harlequin ladybird is known to be aggressive. Describe how this is likely to affect the native ladybirds. Use ideas about competition in your answer. [2]

....

....

....

[Total: .... / 6]

1. This question is about adaptations.

    (a) Complete the following passage. Use words from the list. [3]

    environment   population   features   community   characteristics
    survival   evolutionary   predatory   suited

    Adaptations are special .... or .... which make a living

    organism particularly well .... to its .... Adaptations

    are part of an .... process that increases a living organism's chance of

    ....

    (b) Polar bears are found throughout the Arctic. They spend most of their time on ice floes and tend to stay close to the water when on the mainland. Seals form the basis of their diet.

    Describe **two** adaptations that help polar bears to survive in the icy wilderness of the Arctic. [2]

    ....

    ....

    (c) Prey have many adaptations which help them evade predators. The **ibex** (below) is such an animal.

    Describe **two** adaptations which would help the ibex evade capture. [2]

    ....

    ....

    [Total: .... / 7]

2. A new species of insectivorous mammal has been discovered in Borneo. It was observed in both rainforest undergrowth and more open 'savannah-like' areas. To find out more about it, scientists studied the diet of the creature, which they named a Long-nosed Batink. They obtained this data:

Food	Ants	Termites	Aphids	Beetles	Maggots	Bugs	Grubs
Mass eaten per day/g	275	380	320	75	150	20	110

(a) Plot this data as a bar chart in the grid below. [3]

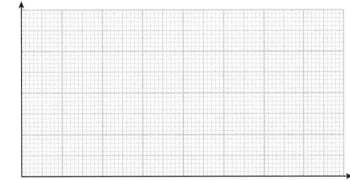

Mass eaten per day/g

(b) Calculate the **percentage** of the Batink's diet which is made up from **termites.**
Show your working. [2]

....

....

(c) The scientists concluded that the Batink had survived many millions of years because of its strategy of being a 'generalist'. Give **two** pieces of evidence from the observations which suggest that the Batink is a generalist. [2]

....

....

[Total: .... / 7]

1. As the environment changes, species must also change if they are going to survive. Choose the correct words from the options given to complete the following sentences. [2]

selection   **adapted**   **slow**   **genes**   **evolved**

Evolution suggests that all living things have _____ from simple life forms

developed billions of years ago. The process is _____ and continual. Evolution

enables organisms to become better _____ to their environment. Adaptations are

controlled by _____ and can therefore be passed on to offspring.

2. Neo-Darwinists are scientists who have accepted Darwin's theory of Natural Selection but have built upon it with new ideas. They have developed the theory because of new evidence that has been found.

(a) One of Darwin's main ideas was that successful characteristics can be passed on to the next generation. How might studies of inheritance have provided further evidence for this? [1]

_____

_____

(b) New evidence and thinking suggests that evolution of new species might happen much more quickly than previously thought. Why did earlier scientists think that long periods of time were needed? Use ideas about **mutation** and **survival** in your answer. [3]

_____

_____

_____

_____

(c) Explain how antibiotic-resistant bacteria can arise due to overuse of antibiotics. In your answer use ideas about **variation**, **survival** and **inheritance**. [3]

_____

_____

_____

_____

[Total: _____ / 9]

Higher Tier

3. The following data is an estimate of the average number of peppered moths spotted in a survey in the centre of Manchester in the summer months before and after the Industrial Revolution.

Month	Pre-Industrial Revolution		Post-Industrial Revolution	
	Pale	Dark	Pale	Dark
June	1261	102	87	1035
July	1247	126	108	1336
August	1272	93	72	1019

(a) Determine the mean number of each colour of moth during the summer and present these figures in the table below. [2]

Pre-Industrial Revolution		Post-Industrial Revolution	
Pale	Dark	Pale	Dark

(b) Draw a bar graph to represent your results. [2]

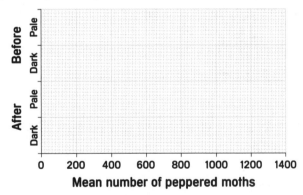

(c) Explain why there were more pale-coloured moths than dark-coloured moths before the Industrial Revolution. [1]

....

(d) Explain why the number of dark-coloured peppered moths increased significantly after the Industrial Revolution. [2]

....

....

....

....

[Total: .... / 7]

1. The growing human population is creating three major issues: increased use of finite resources, increased pollution, and increased competition for basic resources. Which of the following are **not** finite resources? Ring all the correct answers that apply. [1]

   sea water   wind   wood   coal   minerals   oil

2. Images from satellite photography show that there is a hole in the ozone layer.

   (a) Name the main gaseous pollutant thought to be responsible for this hole. _____ [1]

   (b) Explain how a hole in the Earth's ozone layer might lead to increased rates of skin cancer. [2]

3. **(a)** Complete the diagram by labelling the processes involved in the greenhouse effect. [2]

   A _____

   B _____

   (b) Explain how rising average global temperatures may have an effect on the Earth. Use the headings below to structure your answer. [3]

   Climate belts _____

   Sea levels _____

   Ice caps and glaciers _____

4. A sampling exercise was carried out on a short section of river running by a sewage processing plant. The following results were obtained:

Blood worm	Mayfly nymph	Rat-tailed maggot	Leech	Water louse
4	1	3	2	8

Scientists on the sampling team also measured a pH of 6 in the river water and high nitrate levels.

(a) What is the total population of invertebrates in this sample? _____ [1]

(b) What is the total number of species in the sample? _____ [1]

(c) The scientists who obtained the sample concluded that the water was slightly polluted.
State whether you agree with them or not and give a reason. [2]

Do you agree? **Yes/No** _____

Reason _____

_____

(d) What name is given to these invertebrates when used to assess pollution levels? [1]

_____

[Total: _____ **/ 14]**

Higher Tier

5. At the moment, the human population is increasing exponentially.

(a) Sketch a graph on the axes
which shows this increase. [2]

(b) On the y-axis, add a suitable unit for the
population. [1]

(c) Suggest **two** reasons for this 'population
explosion'. [2]

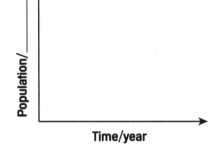

_____

_____

[Total: _____ **/ 5]**

1. The waters around Britain have seen their fish stocks change rapidly since the 1960s. Study the graph below.

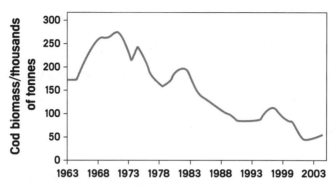

(a) What was the estimated cod biomass in 1978? [1]

.... thousand tonnes

(b) Describe the change in cod numbers between 1978 and 2003. [2]

....

....

(c) International fishing quotas are set in order to manage the numbers of fish in our seas. The table below shows some data about fishing quotas set by an international fishing commission.

Fish species	UK quota 2009/tonnes	UK quota 2010/tonnes
Cod	11,216	13,123
Haddock	27,507	23,381
Whiting	8,426	3,287

(i) By how much did the cod quota change between 2009 and 2010? [1]

.... tonnes

(ii) Suggest possible reasons for the decreased quota for haddock. [2]

....

....

(d) State **one other** measure which fisheries councils can make to prevent over-fishing. [1]

....

2. In Ireland, four species of bumble bee are now designated as endangered. Scientists are worried that numbers may fall so low that they are inadequate to provide pollination to certain plants. State **two** reasons why some organisms become endangered. [2]

....

....

3. People who want to conserve whale species are trying a number of different methods. Describe the **advantages** and **disadvantages** of each method. [6]

Method	Advantages	Disadvantages
Breed whales in captivity in zoos		
Protect natural habitat		
Make whale hunting illegal		

[Total: .... / 15]

Higher Tier

4. Governments and organisations often have to make balanced decisions about the sustainability of species because the needs of a growing population conflict with this. For each of the following conservation programmes, suggest how human needs might conflict with them.

(a) Placing a ban on hunting rhino in South Africa. [1]

....

....

(b) Preventing the burning of moorland heather in Scotland to allow the biodiversity of plants to increase. [1]

....

....

(c) Stopping the removal of hedgerows by farmers on agricultural land. [1]

....

....

[Total: .... / 3]

1. Look at the list of time periods.

    10 years   **hundreds of years**   **thousands of years**   **millions of years**

    How long does it take for a fossil fuel to form?   [1]

    Choose from the list. ....

2. Write about **one** environmental risk associated with transporting crude oil.   [1]

    ....

3. This diagram shows a fractionating column.

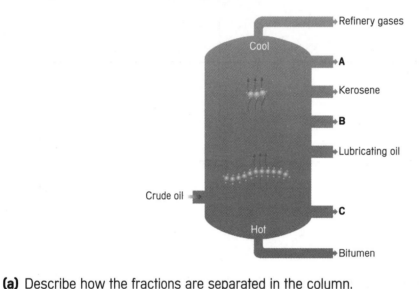

    (a) Describe how the fractions are separated in the column.   [3]

    ....

    ....

    ....

    (b) Name the fractions **A**, **B** and **C**.   [3]

    A ....   **B** ....   **C** ....

4. Explain why crude oil is non-renewable.   [2]

    ....

    ....

5. Look at the diagram of the apparatus used in the laboratory for cracking long-chain hydrocarbons.

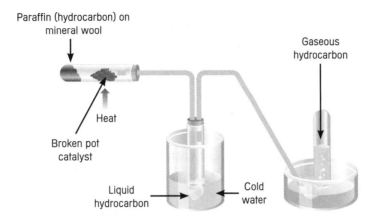

Paraffin (hydrocarbon) on mineral wool

Gaseous hydrocarbon

Heat

Broken pot catalyst

Liquid hydrocarbon

Cold water

(a) Explain what is meant by **cracking long-chain hydrocarbons**.   [2]

_____

_____

(b) What is the purpose of the broken pot catalyst?   [1]

_____

(c) Name **two** useful substances made by cracking.   [2]

_____ **and** _____

6. Look at the bar chart showing the economic demand for the fraction of crude oil and the relative amounts of each fraction in crude oil.

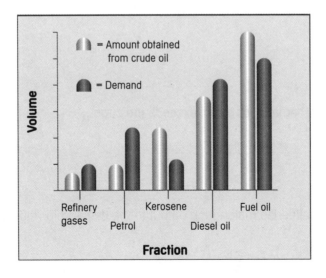

= Amount obtained from crude oil

= Demand

Volume

Refinery gases   Petrol   Kerosene   Diesel oil   Fuel oil

Fraction

(a) Which fraction is in least demand? _____   [1]

(b) Name the fraction where the amount obtained is equal to twice the demand.   [1]

_____

(c) Apart from petrol, name **two** other fractions where demand exceeds supply. [2]

.... **and** ....

[Total: .... / 19]

Higher Tier

7. (a) How does the strength of the bonds between the atoms of a hydrocarbon compare with the strength of the forces of attraction between its molecules? [1]

    ....

    ....

    (b) The boiling point of propane (C_3H_8) is less than 25°C and the boiling point of a larger molecule such as decane ($C_{10}H_{22}$) is higher. Use suitable drawings to explain why. [3]

8. Explain how the difference in the strength of intermolecular forces between hydrocarbons allows them to be separated by fractional distillation. [3]

    ....

    ....

    ....

9. (a) Suggest why the demand for petrol exceeds the supply. [2]

    ....

    ....

    (b) Explain how oil refineries match their output to the demand for different fractions. [3]

    ....

    ....

    ....

    ....

[Total: .... / 12]

1. **(a)** What is another name for burning? _____ [1]

(b) Name the **two** substances that are always made when a hydrocarbon fuel burns completely. [2]

_____ **and** _____

(c) Complete the **word** equation for the complete combustion of methane.

methane + oxygen ➡ _____ + _____ [1]

2. **(a)** Name the gas made when a fuel burns without enough oxygen. _____ [1]

(b) Outline the problem caused by this gas. [1]

_____

(c) Complete this **word** equation showing **incomplete** combustion.

ethane + oxygen ➡ _____ + water [1]

3. Describe **three** advantages of using a blue Bunsen flame rather than using a yellow flame to heat a beaker of water. [3]

_____

_____

_____

4. Look at the diagram of the apparatus to detect the products of burning methane.

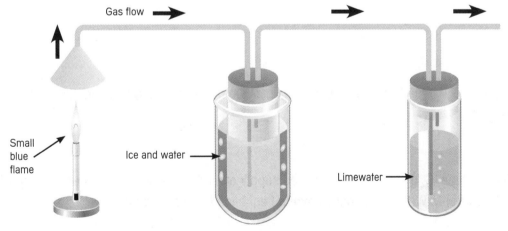

Gas flow

Small blue flame

Ice and water

Limewater

(a) (i) Describe the purpose of the ice and water surrounding the first flask. What would you expect to see inside the flask after a few minutes? [2]

_____

_____

(ii) Name the product of burning that this test detects. _____ [1]

(b) (i) Describe what you would see happening to the limewater after a few minutes. [1]

_____

(ii) Name the product of burning that this test detects. _____ [1]

5. Phil and Nick are going camping. They need to choose a camping stove. Look at the information about each stove.

Stove	Fuel	Energy (kJ/g)	Buying fuel	Flammability of fuel
A	Liquid fuel	1400	Supermarkets	Good
B	Gas fuel	1225	Camping store	Very good
C	Solid fuel	1650	Garages	Poor

Which stove would you suggest they use? Give **two** reasons for your choice. [2]

_____

_____

[Total: _____ / 17]

Higher Tier

6. Explain why the amount of fossil fuels used worldwide is increasing every year. [2]

_____

_____

7. Propane (C_3H_8) burns completely in oxygen. Write the balanced **symbol** equation for this reaction. [2]

_____

8. When butane (C_4H_{10}) burns in a reduced supply of air the reaction makes carbon monoxide and water only. Write the balanced **symbol** equation for this reaction. [2]

_____

[Total: _____ / 6]

1. The data below shows the difference in the composition of the Earth's atmosphere now compared to 4.5 billion years ago.

Gas	Composition of atmosphere 4.5 billion years ago (%)	Composition of atmosphere today (%)
Carbon dioxide	95	0.035
	0	21
Nitrogen	0	
Other gases	5 (ammonia)	about 1 (no ammonia)

(a) Complete the table by filling in the blanks. [2]

(b) Explain why carbon dioxide levels have changed from 4.5 billion years ago to today's value. [2]

2. Pollution problems are caused by some gases. Draw a line to link each gas with the problem it causes. [2]

Carbon monoxide		Photochemical smog
Sulfur dioxide		Acid rain
Nitrogen dioxide		Toxic

3. (a) What causes the formation of carbon monoxide in a car engine? [1]

(b) Name the major pollutant gas made in a catalytic converter. [1]

4. Explain why the amount of carbon dioxide in the Earth's atmosphere is slowly increasing. [3]

5. Describe some of the effects acid rain has on our environment and the organisms that live in it. [2]

....

....

[Total: .... / 13]

6. The following statements describe the process by which the Earth's atmosphere has changed. Place them in order in the boxes given, to show the sequence in which scientists now believe these various stages occurred. [2]

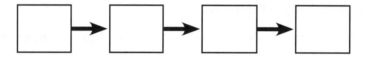

A Oceans formed as the temperature at the surface fell below 100°C.

B Photosynthesis released oxygen into the atmosphere and used up carbon dioxide.

C Nitrifying bacteria used up ammonia and released nitrogen.

D Hot volcanic Earth released carbon dioxide and ammonia into the atmosphere.

7. The sequence you have just worked out to answer **Q6** is just a theory.

(a) What do we mean by a **theory**? [1]

....

....

(b) Explain why the above sequence can only be a theory. [1]

....

8. Describe what causes the formation of nitrogen dioxide in a car engine. [1]

....

9. **(a)** Complete the following **word** equation for the reaction in a catalytic converter. [1]

carbon monoxide + nitrogen oxide ⟶ .... + ...

(b) Complete and balance the following **symbol** equation for the reaction in a catalytic converter that produces nitrogen and carbon dioxide. [2]

$CO + NO$ ⟶ .... + ...

[Total: .... / 8]

1. Butane is an alkane. Explain the meaning of the term **alkane**. [1]

_____

2. Look at these diagrams which show the displayed formulae of some hydrocarbons.

(a) Select which structures are correctly displayed formulae of **alkanes**. [2]

(b) Select which structure has the molecular formula C_4H_{10}. [1]

3. **(a)** Ethene is an alkene. Explain the meaning of the term **alkene**. [1]

_____

(b) Describe the difference between an **alkane** and an **alkene**. [2]

_____

_____

(c) Draw the displayed formulae for **ethene** (C_2H_4) and **ethane** (C_2H_6). [2]

Ethene   **Ethane**

4. **(a)** What is a monomer? [2]

_____

_____

(b) Describe what happens in a polymerisation reaction. [3]

_____

_____

_____

5. **(a)** Propene is an alkene that can form a long-chain molecule (polymer). Name the polymer made

from propene. _____ [1]

(b) Name this type of polymerisation. _____ [1]

(c) What are the conditions needed for polymerisation? [2]

_____

_____

[Total: _____ **/ 18]**

Higher Tier

6. **(a)** Complete the following equation to show how four propene molecules join together to form
part of its polymer. [3]

(b) Look at the displayed formula of a polymer. Draw the monomer used to make it. [2]

7. Alkenes are a series of unsaturated hydrocarbons. Explain this statement. [2]

_____

_____

8. Describe how bromine water can be used to test for an alkene. Include in your answer what type
of reaction is involved and the product of a positive test. [3]

_____

_____

_____

_____

[Total: _____ **/ 10]**

1. Describe the properties of poly(ethene) that make it suitable to make shopping carrier bags. [2]

2. (a) Explain the term **biodegradable**. [1]

(b) Suggest **two** materials that are biodegradable. [2]

_____ **and** _____

(c) Why is it important to develop plastics that are biodegradable? [2]

3. (a) Take-away coffee cups are made from expanded polystyrene. Write about some of its properties. [2]

(b) Suggest the **two** most important properties that nylon has that enable it to be used as climbing rope. [2]

_____ **and** _____

4. What are the **three** main ways of disposing of plastic? In your answer you should give a **disadvantage** for each method.

✎ *The quality of your written communication will be assessed in this question.* [6]

[Total: _____ / 17]

5. **(a)** Describe how Gore-tex® is made from layers of nylon and PTFE. You may wish to use a diagram. [2]

(b) Why does the PTFE layer in Gore-tex® need a nylon layer? [1]

(c) Explain how Gore-tex® is rainproof but allows perspiration (sweat) to travel through it. [2]

6. Describe **three** ways in which the properties of a polymer are changed when the long-chain molecules are cross-linked. [3]

7. Explain why nylon is a strong material but when it is heated it can be stretched and shaped. Use ideas about **forces** within and between molecules. [4]

[Total: .... / 12]

1. Outline **two** reasons why baking bread is a chemical change. [2]

_____ **and** _____

2. Describe the reason for adding an antioxidant to a food. [1]

_____

3. Draw a line to link the ingredient with its property. [2]

Eggs		Gives off carbon dioxide when cooked
Emulsifier		Helps oil and water mix
Baking powder		Good source of protein

4. Some food additives improve the appearance of the food. Suggest **two** other reasons why food additives are put in food. [2]

_____

_____

5. Complete the **word** equation to show the decomposition of baking powder. [1]

sodium hydrogencarbonate ➡ _____ + _____ + _____

6. Explain the meaning of the word **hydrophobic**. _____ [1]

[Total: _____ / 9]

Higher Tier

7. Explain how cooking a potato makes it easier to digest. [3]

_____

_____

8. What happens to protein molecules when they are heated and cooked? [3]

_____

_____

9. Write down the balanced **symbol** equation for the thermal decomposition of sodium hydrogencarbonate. [2]

_____

[Total: _____ / 8]

1. What does **synthetic** mean? [1]

2. A perfume must smell nice and not irritate your skin. Suggest a reason why each of the following properties of a perfume are also important.

   (a) Evaporates easily. [1]

   (b) Insoluble in water. [1]

3. Complete the general equation. [1]

   alcohol + acid ⟶ _____ + _____

4. Put the list of instructions to make the ester ethyl ethanoate in the correct order. Write 1, 2, 3 or 4 in each box. [2]

   (a) Put some sodium carbonate solution in a beaker. ⬭

   (b) Add 5 cm^3 of ethanol to 5 cm^3 of ethanoic acid in a test tube. ⬭

   (c) Pour the reaction mixture into the sodium carbonate solution. ⬭

   (d) Add two drops of sulfuric acid and wait a few minutes. ⬭

5. **(a)** Why do cosmetics have to be tested before they are sold? [1]

   (b) Cosmetics are sometimes tested on animals.

   (i) What action has the EU taken over the testing of cosmetics on animals? [1]

   (ii) Explain why people have asked the EU to take this action. [2]

6. Draw a line to link each word with its correct description. [2]

A substance that dissolves in a liquid		Solvent
A liquid that does the dissolving		Solution
A mixture of a dissolved solid and a liquid		Solute

7. Look at the table. It shows information about different solvents.

Solvent	Nail varnish	Sodium chloride (salt)
Water	Does not dissolve	Very soluble
Ethanol	Dissolves in 15 seconds	Slightly soluble
Propanone	Dissolves in 2 seconds	Insoluble

(a) Suggest a solvent to use to dissolve a salt such as magnesium bromide. [1]

(b) Grass stains do not dissolve in water. Suggest a solvent to remove grass stains from a white

football shirt. [1]

8. Outline **one** use of an ester. [1]

[Total: .... / 15]

Higher Tier

9. Explain why some people argue that testing cosmetics on animals may be acceptable in some cases. [2]

10. (a) What does **volatile** mean? [1]

(b) Use ideas about forces between particles to explain why ethyl ethanoate is more volatile than water. [3]

11. Use ideas about **forces** between particles to explain why nail varnish will not dissolve in water. [4]

[Total: .... / 10]

1. Look at the words and definitions. Draw a line to link each term with its correct meaning. [2]

Solvent	Strong coloured material
Colloid	Fine solid particles mixed in a liquid
Binding medium	Liquid that dissolves substances
Pigment	Oil that sticks to a surface

2. Marilyn uses an emulsion paint to cover her kitchen wall.

   (a) Explain why she uses paint on the wall. [1]

   ....

   (b) Name the solvent in an emulsion paint. .... [1]

3. Alex has made his own oil paint by mixing a pigment with oil. He finds it is too thick to paint with. Suggest what he should do. [1]

   ....

[Total: .... / 5]

Higher Tier

4. Explain what happens to a gloss paint when it is applied to a window frame and is allowed to 'dry'. [2]

   ....

   ....

5. (a) Describe the undesirable property that the earliest phosphorescent paints had. [1]

   ....

   (b) What problem did this cause? [1]

   ....

   ....

[Total: .... / 4]

OCR Gateway GCSE Science B Workbook Answers

Answering Quality of Written Communication Questions

A number of the questions in your examinations will include an assessment of the quality of your written communication (QWC). These questions are worth a maximum of 6 marks and are indicated by a pencil icon (✏).

Your answers to these questions will be marked according to...
- the level of your understanding of the relevant science
- how well you structure your answer
- the style of your writing, including the quality of your punctuation, grammar and spelling.

QWC questions will be marked using a 'Levels of Response' mark scheme. The examiner will decide whether your answer is in the top level, middle level or bottom level. The expected quality of written communication is different in the three levels and it will always be considered at the same time as looking at the scientific information in your answer:
- To achieve Level 3 (which is the top level and is worth 5–6 marks), your answer should contain relevant science, and be organised and presented in a structured and coherent manner. You should use scientific terms appropriately and your spelling, punctuation and grammar should have very few errors.
- For Level 2 (worth 3–4 marks), there may be more errors in your spelling, punctuation and grammar, and your answer will miss some of the things expected at Level 3.

- For Level 1 (worth 1–2 marks), your answer may be written using simplistic language. You will have included some relevant science, but the quality of your written communication may have limited how well the examiner can understand your answer. This could be due to lots of errors in spelling, punctuation and grammar, misuse of scientific terms or a poor structure.
- An answer given Level 0 may contain insufficient or irrelevant science, and will not be given any marks.

You will be awarded the higher or lower mark within a particular level depending on the quality of the science and the quality of the written communication in your answer.

Even if the quality of your written communication is perfect, the level you are awarded will be limited if you show little understanding of the relevant science, and you will be given Level 0 if you show no relevant scientific understanding at all.

To help you understand the criteria above, three specimen answers are provided to the first QWC question in this workbook. The first is a model answer worth 6 marks, the second answer would be worth 4 marks and the third answer worth 2 marks. The three exemplar answers are differentiated by their scientific content and use of scientific terminology. Model answers worth 6 marks are provided to all other QWC questions to help you aspire to the best possible marks.

Biology

B1: Understanding Organisms

Pages 3–4

1. (a) $\frac{364}{4}$ = 91

   (1 mark for correct answer, 1 mark for showing working.)
   (b) **Any two from**: Decrease alcohol intake; Reduce stress; Work fewer hours; Reduce salt intake; Reduce fat intake in diet.
   (c) Resting rate higher; Time for pulse to return to resting rate is longer.
   (d) YES – Jim is free from infection, but his heart monitor information shows that he is not as capable of carrying out physical exercise as Bob.
   Or NO – Jim is neither fit nor healthy as his physical well-being is limited by high blood pressure/prone to heart disease.
2. (a) Thrombus **or** thrombosis
   (b) **Vessel blocked**: Coronary artery **(1 mark)**
   Explanation: Oxygen/glucose is prevented from reaching the heart muscle; So the heart muscle dies/becomes scarred/can no longer respire.
3. Carbon monoxide combines irreversibly with haemoglobin, in red blood cells/carbon monoxide has a higher affinity for oxygen; Oxygen can no longer bind with haemoglobin/enter red blood cell.
4. (a) **Any two from**: Burst blood vessels; Damage to brain; Stroke; Kidney damage; Heart attack.
   (b) **Any one of**: Dizziness; Fainting; Poor circulation.

Pages 5–6

1. (a) Carbohydrates **and** fats **should be ringed. (Both required for 1 mark.)**
   (b) Vitamin C is important for a healthy diet because it prevents scurvy and is essential for healthy skin and gums.

(c) Fibre
2. (a) $\frac{66}{1.54^2}$ = 28 (to nearest whole number). **(1 mark for correct answer, 1 mark for showing working.)**
   (b) Karen is slightly overweight so she needs to lose some weight.
3. (a) 0.6 × 63 = 37.8 g **(1 mark for correct answer, 1 mark for showing working.)** Elouise should eat at least 2.8 g more **(1 mark)**.
   (b) Protein is needed for growth and teenagers grow rapidly.
   (c) 2nd class protein
4. (a) Value estimated between 14.0% and 14.3%.
   (b) Storage product is glycogen; Found in liver/muscles.

Pages 7–8

1. Bacteria – Cholera; Fungi – Athlete's foot; Viruses – Flu; Protozoa – malaria. **(Four correct = 3 marks, subtract 1 mark for every incorrect link, subtract 1 mark for multiple lines.)**
2. (a) Mosquitoes are vectors; Which transfer the malaria/parasite (a protozoan).
   (b) Engulf/digest bacteria.
   (c) Damage Harriet's cells/produce toxins.
3. **Animal testing**
   Advantage: Any one of: Chosen animals, e.g. mice, have similar organs and systems to humans so make good models; Can screen potential problems with side effects.
   Disadvantage: Any one of: Many people think this is cruel and does not respect animal life; Animal systems may respond differently to human systems.
   Computer modelling
   Advantage: Any one of: Does not involve a living organism; Low cost – animals not involved.
   Disadvantage: Can only predict effect of new drugs based on knowledge of old ones.
4. (a) (i) Phagocytes engulf pathogen, then digest it **(1 mark)**.
       (ii) Antibodies lock on to antigen/pathogen/Clump pathogens together **(1 mark)**.

(b) The vaccine contains dead/heat-treated pathogen/microbe. **(1 mark)**
Any three from: Antigen recognised as foreign/non-self; Lymphocytes produce antibodies against it; Memory cells (specialised white blood cells) remain in system; Ready to produce antibodies if re-infection occurs.
(c) Antibiotics do not work against viruses; Over-prescription may lead to resistant bacteria.
5. Subjects of experiment do not know whether they are receiving the active ingredient or the placebo; Scientists, e.g. doctors, do not know who they are administering the active ingredient and the placebo to.

Pages 9–11

1. (a) Nucleus
   (b) Cell body **or** cytoplasm.
2. (a) Central nervous system
   (b) Receptors sense/detect stimuli; And transfer nervous information/impulses through sensory neurones; To the brain.
3. (a) The response is automatic/unconscious; Response is rapid.
   (b) **Any four from**: Sensor/(pain) receptor detects stimulus/pin; Sensory neurone transmits impulse to CNS/spine; Relay neurone passes impulse on; Impulse sent down motor neurone; To effector/arm muscle.
4. (a) A–3; B–1; C–2; D–4
   (b) Light rays fall on the cornea where they are refracted/bent; The lens then refracts/bends light further.
   (c) Enables rabbits to have an almost 360° view to detect approaching predators.
5. Human **(no marks)**; Time for impulse to travel in human is quicker/lower; By 0.00014 s/Compare 0.0015 s in human with 0.0019 s in cockroach.
6. (a) Synapse
   (b) **Elongated shape** to carry impulses over long distances; **Fatty sheath** to speed up nervous transmission; **Branched endings** to make connections with many other nerve cells.
   (c) **Any three from**: Transmitter substance released at end of 1st neurone in response to impulse; Travels across synaptic cleft by diffusion; Transmitter binds with receptor molecules on next neurone; Impulse released in 2nd neurone.

Pages 12–13

1. Nicotine – stimulant; Alcohol – depressant; Paracetamol – painkiller; Tamazepan – sedative.
2. (a) A class A drug carries higher penalties; Class A drugs are deemed to be more harmful.
   (b) A psychological or physical need for something which makes you want more of it (a craving).
   (c) He has to use larger amounts; To get the same effects.
   (d) **Any two from**: Psychological problems; Sweating; Stomach cramps; Shaking; Nausea; Cravings.
3. (a) 20 x
   (b) **Any two from**: Cigarette smoke causes alveoli/air sac walls to collapse; Lower surface area slows down diffusion rate for gases; Gaseous exchange less efficient; Therefore person becomes breathless.
   (c) **Any one of**: Bronchitis; Heart disease; Stroke.
4. **Stimulants**: **A description or diagram to show**: Stimulant increasing production of transmitter substance; Increasing level of activity in nervous system.
   Depressants: **A description or diagram to show any two from**: Depressant binding with receptor molecule in synapse; Blocking transmission of impulse; Leads to lower nervous system activity.

Pages 14–15

1. (a) Homeostasis
   (b) Blood sugar; Water
   (c) **Any two from**: Muscle contraction; Generates heat; Through respiration.
   (d) **Any two from**: Evaporation of water from skin; Takes in heat from skin; Radiation; Endothermic change.

(e) 37°C
(f) To enable enzymes to work at their optimum temperature.
2. **Gland**: pancreas, **Hormones**: insulin
3. (a) Hormone controls insulin; Which can control blood sugar level.
   (b) People with type 2 diabetes can often control their sugar levels by adjusting their diet.
4. (a) The person's blood sugar level **(1 mark)** fluctuates dramatically **(1 mark)**.
   (b) The person will have eaten their breakfast and dinner at points **A** and **B** respectively.
   (c) There would have been a slight rise, followed by a swift drop back to the normal level.
   (d) Because their blood sugar level dropped.

Page 16

1. (a) Light; Gravity
   (b) The upper extension is the shoot **(1 mark)** and lower extension is the root **(1 mark)**.
   (c) It is growing against the force of gravity.
   (d) Negative geotropism **or** negative gravitropism.
2. Plant hormones **should be ticked**.
3. **This is a model answer which would score the full 6 marks**: Miriam would take 100 seeds of the same mass and grow them in two trays of the same compost with an equal spacing between them. One tray would be put in a dark place with a single light source (e.g. lamp) shining from one direction. The other tray (the control) would be put in a place with plenty of light. Over five days she would give both trays of shoots equal measures of water. After five days the seeds with shoots are removed. Miriam would find that most, if not all, the shoots in the first tray had grown towards the lamp (light source) and the shoots in the second tray would have grown vertically. The experiment could be repeated to increase the reliability of the observations.
   This answer would score 4 marks: Miriam would take 100 seeds and plant them in two trays. One tray would be in a dark place and have a lamp shining on it and the other would be in lots of light. She would water both trays. After five days she would find that the shoots in the first tray grow towards the light source and the shoots in the second tray grow straight up.
   This answer would score 2 marks: Miriam would plant 100 seeds in trays. One tray would have a lamp shining on it and the other would be in lots of light. After a few days the plants in the first tray will have grown towards the lamp.

Pages 17–19

1. Nucleus – Cell structure that contains the chromosomes
   Chromosomes – Consist of large numbers of genes
   Genes – Small pieces of DNA that control the development of a characteristic
   Alleles – Different forms of the same gene
   (3 marks for four correct answers, subtract 1 mark for every incorrect link, subtract 1 mark for multiple lines.)
2. Red blood cell – 0; Sperm cell – 23; Skin cell – 46; Ovum – 23
   (All correct = 3, subtract 1 for every incorrect response.)
3. (a) (i) Combination; (ii) Genetics; (iii) Combination; (iv) Environment; (v) Environment; (vi) Combination **(4 marks for all correct, subtract 1 mark for every incorrect response.)**
   (b) George and Nathan's parents produced many unique/ genetically different gametes; These gametes randomly fused/joined during fertilisation.
   (c) Olwen has XX, George has XY.
   (d) Cystic fibrosis is inherited, not infectious; Can only be transferred from parents.
4. (a) 39
   (b) Black is the dominant gene/allele/White is recessive **(1 mark, note: not given for references to 'black chromosome' or 'white chromosome')**; The gene for black fur is passed on/ inherited **from the father (1 mark)**.

(c) **1st mark for**: correct genotype for both parents Bb and bb or correct gametes Bb and bb; **2nd mark for**: genotype of offspring correct Bb and bb; **3rd mark for**: showing correct phenotype of offspring **(see below in terms of diagrams)**.

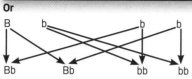

	b	b
B	Bb Black	Bb Black
b	bb White	bb White

Or

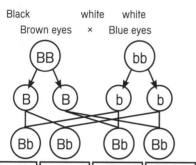

B   b   b   b

Bb   Bb   bb   bb

Black   Black   white   white

5. (a)

Brown eyes × Blue eyes

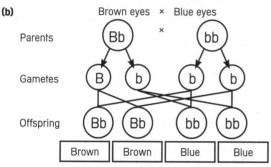

Parents   BB   bb

Gametes   B   B   b   b

Offspring   Bb   Bb   Bb   Bb

| Brown | Brown | Brown | Brown |

(1 mark will be awarded for each correct row.)

(b)

Brown eyes × Blue eyes

Parents   Bb   ×   bb

Gametes   B   b   b   b

Offspring   Bb   Bb   bb   bb

| Brown | Brown | Blue | Blue |

(1 mark will be awarded for each correct row.)

(c) If both parents have heterozygous genes (e.g. Bb) **(1 mark)**; then there is a (one in four) chance of the child having blue eyes **(1 mark)**.

Brown eyes × Brown eyes

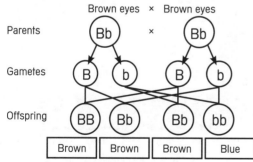

Parents   Bb   ×   Bb

Gametes   B   b   B   b

Offspring   BB   Bb   Bb   bb

| Brown | Brown | Brown | Blue |

(2 marks for correct diagram.)

6. (a)

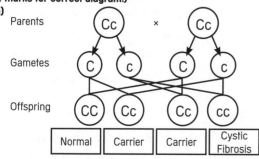

Parents   Cc   ×   Cc

Gametes   C   c   C   c

Offspring   CC   Cc   Cc   cc

| Normal | Carrier | Carrier | Cystic Fibrosis |

(1 mark will be awarded for each correct row.)

(b) There was a one in four chance/0.25/25%

(c) Heterozygous **should be ringed**.

B2: Understanding Our Environment

Pages 20–21

1. annelids; molluscs; crustaceans; arachnids **should be ringed.**
    (Four correct = 3 marks, three correct = 2 marks, two correct = 1 mark, zero or one correct = 0 marks.)

2. (a) They cannot produce fertile offspring.
    (b) (i) **Underline any one of the following**: 'carnivorous big cats'; 'five toes on their front paws and four toes on their back paws'; 'claws can be drawn back'.
        (ii) Leopards are more closely related to tigers **(1 mark)**. Both are the *Panthera* genus/snow leopards are a different genus **(1 mark)**.

3. (a) Possesses features which are found in reptiles and birds, e.g. feathers place it with birds but it also has teeth like reptiles; It is an intermediate form.
    (b) **Any two from**: Bacteria reproduce asexually; Therefore difficult to apply concept of 'fertile' offspring; Observable features may often be identical, have to use special stains as a classification tool.
    (c) Similar organisms have similar DNA sequencing; Scientists can look for a close match of DNA to work out relatedness of different groups/species/strains.

Pages 22–23

1. Transfer of energy **should be ticked**.
2. (a) A producer is an organism which produces its own food.
    (b) Sunlight/the sun
    (c) **Any one of**: Wasp; Ladybird; Hoverfly
    (d) Diagram **B**
    (e) **Any two from**: Respiration; Reproduction; Egestion (faeces); Movement/muscle contraction in animals; Maintaining body temperature.
3. (a) **Any one of**: Plant material; Grass; Cereal crops; Sileage.
    (b) Movement **and** respiration
    (c) 6000 − (2000 + 3000) = 6000 − 5000 = 1000 kJ
4. (a) $\frac{1000}{6000}$ × 100 = 17% **(1 mark for correct answer, 1 mark for showing working.)**
    (b) Cellulose in plant material requires more energy to digest **(1 mark)**; therefore larger amounts need to be consumed **(1 mark)**. **Accept converse argument for humans.**
    (c) **This is a model answer, which demonstrates QWC, and would therefore score the full 6 marks**: Shorter food chains are more energy efficient because they have fewer trophic levels. A vegetarian food chain may have only two levels: plants – humans, whereas a meat-eating diet will have three or more. We know that energy is lost at each consumer trophic level as respiration, heat, excretion, egestion and movement. In this way, a consumer may lose up to 90% energy. Producing food for a vegetarian population requires decreased areas of land because at least one trophic level is removed from the food chain. A field of wheat will support many more humans than a field of cattle. This can be seen in a pyramid of biomass where the width of the human trophic level is greater when humans are a primary consumer compared with when they are a secondary or tertiary consumer.

Pages 24–25

1. (a) Respiration
    (b) **Any two from**: Fossil fuels represent a carbon 'sink'/They absorbed great quantities of carbon dioxide many millions of years ago; Combustion in power stations returns this carbon dioxide to the atmosphere; Less burning of fossil fuels cuts down on carbon emissions; Alternative sources of energy may not return as much carbon dioxide to the atmosphere.
2. (a) Nitrogen is too unreactive to be incorporated directly into an animal's body. Animals do not possess the necessary enzymes/adaptations to do this.
    (b) **A** = 1, **B** = 3, **C** = 4, **D** = 2 **(All four correct = 2 marks. Subtract 1 mark for every incorrect answer.)**

3. **(a)** Peat contains fossilised remains of plants **(1 mark)**; which originally absorbed carbon dioxide from the atmosphere via photosynthesis **(1 mark)**.
   (b) **Any two of**: Eruption of volcanoes adjacent to limestone deposits; Acid rain; Chemical weathering of limestone.
4. **(a)** Nitrogen-fixing bacteria
   (b) They convert nitrogen to nitrates **(1 mark)**, which can be absorbed by plants **(1 mark)**.
   (c) Nitrates
   (d) Clover has nitrate in its roots, formed by a mutualistic relationship with bacteria **(1 mark)**, so clover ploughed back into the soil fertilises it **(1 mark)**.

Pages 26–27

1. **(a)**

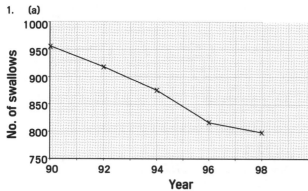

(2 marks for correct plotting, 1 mark for accurate joining of points.)
   (b) 775 (+ 1 − 10)
   (c) Flying insects are prey for swallows **(1 mark)**; so if there are fewer insects there is less food for swallows **(1 mark)**.
2. **(a)**

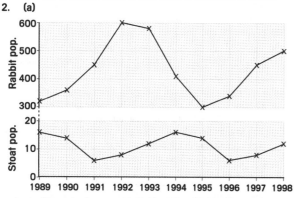

(2 marks for correct plotting, 1 mark for joining of points.)
   (b) As the rabbit population decreases, there is less food (the rabbits) available for the stoats **(1 mark)**; so the stoat population decreases **(1 mark)**; fewer rabbits are eaten, so the rabbit population increases **(1 mark)**.
3. **(a)** Bacteria convert nitrogen from the air into nitrates. Leguminous plants absorb nitrates and use them to make plant proteins; Pea plants are therefore able to survive in poor soils with low nitrate levels because of these bacteria.
   (b) Plants make sugars by photosynthesis which bacteria absorb and use for respiration to get energy.
4. **(a)** Niche is the role or 'job description' which an organism carries out in its habitat.
   (b) When two types of ladybird occupy the same niche they compete for the same resources; The native ladybirds are at a competitive disadvantage so are likely to decline in number.

Pages 28–29

1. **(a)** features; characteristics; suited; environment; evolutionary; survival. **(six words correct = 3 marks, four or five words correct = 2 marks, two or three words correct = 1 mark, one or 0 words correct = 0 marks)**.
   (b) **Any two from**: Small ears, reducing heat loss; Insulating fat/ blubber; Thick insulating fur; Fur on soles of feet for

insulation; Powerful legs for chasing prey; Sharp claws and teeth for shearing flesh.
   (c) **Any two from**: Eyes at side of head for a wide field of vision; Well-camouflaged; Built for speed/muscular legs for fast running.
2. **(a)**

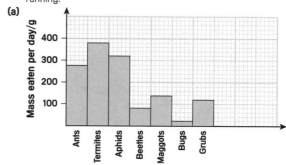

(2 marks for correct plotting of bars, 1 mark for correct labeling of x and y axes.)
   (b) $\frac{380}{1330}$ = 28.6% **(1 mark for correct answer, 1 mark for showing working.)**
   (c) Batink occupies more than one habitat/niche; Eats a wide variety of food/prey.

Pages 30–31

1. evolved, slow; adapted; genes. **(Four words correct = 2 marks, two or three words correct = 1 mark, one or zero words correct = 0 marks.)**
2. **(a)** **Any one of**: Discovery of DNA/genes/units of inheritance in cells; Carry code for characteristics; Shown to be passed on to offspring.
   (b) **Any three from**: Mutations/changes in base sequence are rare; Mutations usually harmful; Advantageous characteristics/genes/alleles might not be selected for; Time required for small changes to result in new species.
   (c) Natural variation within bacterial population leads to occasional 'mutations', which are resistant to antibiotics; These survive to pass on genes to next generation, natural strain of bacteria cannot survive/killed by antibiotics; Resistant bacteria remain, and original strain becomes extinct.
3. **(a)** **Pre-Industrial Revolution**; Pale: 1260; Dark: 107 **(1 mark)**. **Post-Industrial Revolution**; Pale: 89; Dark: 1130 **(1 mark)**.
   (b)

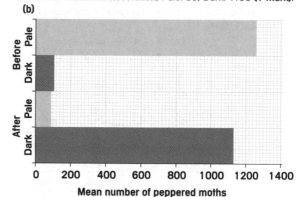

(2 marks for correct plotting of bars.)
   (c) Because they were better camouflaged against the silver birch tree bark.
   (d) **Any two from**: Dark peppered moths would be more camouflaged than pale moths after the Industrial Revolution; Due to the effects of air pollution; Dark moths have increased chance of survival and consequently chance of reproducing and passing on their genes.

Pages 32–33

1. sea water **and** wind **and** wood **should be ringed for 1 mark**.
2. **(a)** CFCs
   (b) An increase in UV radiation **(1 mark)**; causes skin cells to mutate, which causes melanoma/tumours **(1 mark)**.

3. (a) **A** UV rays from the sun pass through the atmosphere and are absorbed at the surface.
    B infrared radiation cannot 'escape' into space/exit prevented by greenhouse gases.
    (b) **Climate belts** shift causing ecosystems and habitats to change, organisms are displaced and become extinct.
    Sea levels rise causing flooding of coastal regions, islands are inundated and disappear beneath sea level.
    Ice caps and glaciers melt and retreat.
4. (a) 18
    (b) 5
    (c) Yes **(Yes/No answer carries no marks)**: The presence of species which are adapted to polluted environment, e.g. rat-tailed maggot, water louse (low oxygen concentration) pH acidic, nitrate levels high **(2 marks)**. **Or** No **(Yes/No answer carries no marks)**: Species diversity is not too small, mayfly nymphs are present **(2 marks)**.
    (d) Indicator species
5. (a) **see graph**
    (b) **see graph**

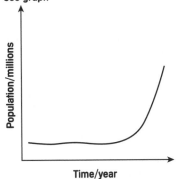

    (c) **Any two from**: Insufficient birth control; Better life expectancy; Better health care

Pages 34–35

1. (a) 160 thousand tonnes **(+ 1 – 10 thousand)**
    (b) Overall decrease in numbers; Temporary rises in 1978–1983 and 1993–1998.
    (c) (i) 1907 tonnes
        (ii) **Any two from**: Numbers of haddock still declined; Therefore less fish should be caught; In order for fish stocks to recover.
    (d) **Any one of**: Increasing mesh size to allow young cod to reach breeding age; Increase quotas of other fish species.
2. **Any two from**: Climate change; New predators; Habitat destruction; Hunting; Competition; Pollution.
3.

	Advantages	Disadvantages
Breed whales in captivity in zoos	Study whales so that we can protect them more efficiently; **or** Possibly return whales born in captivity to natural environment.	Captive whale behaviour is not the same as that of free whales; **or** Poor survival rate of released whales.
Protect natural habitat	Enable whales to live and reproduce in own environment.	Difficult to prevent pollution, fishing, etc. in open sea.
Make whale hunting illegal	Protect whales from culling. Fewer whales die.	Difficult to enforce laws; **or** Some countries feel it is right to hunt whales.

4. (a) Tourism and hunting businesses might suffer if rhinos are protected.
    (b) Maintaining the habitat for grouse shooting is prevented, local economy affected, livelihoods of gamekeepers, etc.
    (c) Prevents farmers enlarging fields and maximising profit on crops, hedges hinder movement of large agricultural machines.

Chemistry

C1: Carbon Chemistry

Pages 36–38

1. millions of years
2. **Any one of:** Oil spills; Oil is toxic to living things/wildlife; Damage to beaches; Damage to birds' feathers, causing death; Detergents used to clean oil also can damage wildlife.
3. (a) Crude oil is boiled/oil **vapour** fed in the bottom of the column **(1 mark); Any two from:** It rises up the column; It starts to cool; It condenses (at its boiling temperature); Removed from column as a liquid.
    (b) **A:** Petrol; **B:** Diesel; **C:** Fuel oil.
4. It takes a long time to make; It is being used up faster than it can be made.
5. (a) Breaking up large hydrocarbon molecules **(1 mark)**; Into more useful, smaller hydrocarbon molecules **(1 mark)**.
    (b) It speeds up the reaction, gives a surface on which the reaction takes place
    (c) Ethene **and** petrol.
6. (a) Refinery gas
    (b) Kerosene
    (c) Refinery gas **and** diesel.
7. (a) The bonds within the molecule are much stronger than the forces between the molecules.
    (b) **(1 mark for each diagram.)**

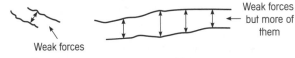

Propane   Decane

        1 extra mark for any of the following: The forces between all the molecules are weak; More force/interaction between bigger molecules; More energy needed to overcome the larger force.
8. Small molecules have small intermolecular forces therefore low boiling temperatures; Large molecules have large intermolecular forces therefore high boiling temperatures; The size of the molecules dictates the temperatures at which the fractions condense.
9. (a) **Any two from:** Most cars use petrol; There are millions of cars; Crude oil contains a small proportion of petrol.
    (b) **Any three from:** Cracking; Is used to break up; Large molecules that are not in demand; To make smaller molecules; That are in demand.

Pages 39–40

1. (a) Combustion
    (b) Water **and** carbon dioxide
    (c) methane + oxygen ⟶ carbon dioxide + water
2. (a) Carbon monoxide
    (b) The gas is toxic/poisonous
    (c) ethane + oxygen ⟶ carbon monoxide + water
3. **Any three from:** You get a hotter flame; The water heats up quicker; There is no soot produced; No carbon monoxide is made.
4. (a) (i) It cools the gases from the flame; Condensation forms inside the flask.
        (ii) Water
    (b) (i) It goes milky/cloudy/white precipitate.
        (ii) Carbon dioxide
5. **1 mark for each reason:**
    A - Fuel energy content good; Easily obtained; Easy to burn.
    B - Fuel energy content alright; Easily obtained; Easy to burn – more controllable.
    C - Fuel energy content very good; Easily obtained.
6. **Any two from:** The world's population is increasing; Some countries (such as China and India) have growing economies; And need more fuel (for development).
7. $C_3H_8 + 5O_2 \longrightarrow 3CO_2 + 4H_2O$ **(1 mark for correct formulae, 1 mark for balancing.)**
8. $2C_4H_{10} + 9O_2 \longrightarrow 8CO + 10H_2O$ **(1 mark for correct formulae, 1 mark for balancing.)**

Pages 41–42

1. (a)

Gas	Composition of atmosphere 4.5 billion years ago (%)	Composition of atmosphere today (%)
Carbon dioxide	95	0.035
Oxygen	0	21
Nitrogen	0	**78**
Other gases	5 (ammonia)	about 1 (no ammonia)

(b) Any two from: Plants have evolved; Remove carbon dioxide from air; By photosynthesis.

2. Carbon monoxide — Photochemical smog
Sulfur dioxide — Acid rain
Nitrogen dioxide — Toxic
(All three correct for 2 marks, one correct for 1 mark.)

3. (a) Incomplete combustion of the fuel.
(b) Carbon dioxide

4. Carbon dioxide is being created faster **(1 mark)**; by combustion/cement production, etc. **(1 mark)**; than can be removed by photosynthesis **(1 mark)**.

5. Any two from: Damages stonework; Kills trees; Kills fish; Corrodes metals; Kills plants.

6. D A C B **(2 marks if all correct, 1 mark if D A or C B correct.)**

7. (a) An idea that is not totally tested but that if true would explain certain facts or phenomena.
(b) No one was there to see it happen.

8. High temperature or the spark from the spark plug.

9. (a) carbon monoxide + nitrogen oxide ⟶ nitrogen + carbon dioxide
(b) $2CO + 2NO \longrightarrow N_2 + 2CO_2$ **(1 mark for correct formulae, 1 mark for balancing.)**

Pages 43–44

1. A hydrocarbon that contains only single bonds.

2. (a) C and D
(b) C

3. (a) A hydrocarbon that contains a carbon-carbon double bond.
(b) An **alkene** contains a carbon-carbon double bond **(1 mark)**; An **alkane** contains only single bonds **(1 mark)**.
(c)

Ethene **(1 mark)**   Ethane **(1 mark)**

4. (a) Small molecules **(1 mark)**; that can be joined together to make a polymer **(1 mark)**.
(b) Any three from: Many small molecules/monomers; Join together; To make a long-chained molecule/polymer; The double bond of alkene monomers breaks enabling the monomers/molecules to bond together.

5. (a) Poly(propene)
(b) Addition polymerisation
(c) Needs a catalyst **and** a high pressure

6. (a)

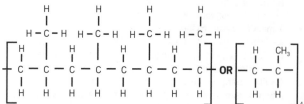

1st diagram above: Chain of eight carbon atoms **(1 mark)**; CH_3 side chain **(1 mark)**; Side chain on every second C atom **(1 mark)**.
2nd diagram above: (1 mark for three single bonds through the middle of the structure, 1 mark for CH_3 group, 1 mark for the four outside the bracket.)

(b)

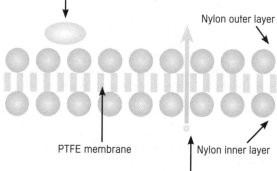

(1 mark for C=C bond, 1 mark if rest correct.)

7. Any two from: Alkenes contain hydrogen and carbon only; They contain two double bond; They do not contain the maximum number of hydrogen atoms.

8. Any three from: Shake a sample of the material with some orange bromine water; If the substance is unsaturated it will go colourless very quickly; If it is saturated it will stay orange; This is an addition reaction; A dibromo compound is made.

Pages 45–46

1. Any two from: Lightweight (low density); Printable; Flexible, Easily shaped.

2. (a) It rots/it breaks down/bacteria will break it down
(b) Any two materials from living things **(1 mark for each answer).**
(c) Biodegradable plastics will rot; They will not take up space in landfill; Lots of plastic is used; Disposal of non-biodegradable plastic is a problem. **(1 mark for one problem, 1 mark for one reason.)**

3. (a) Waterproof; Heat insulator
(b) Any two from: Strong; Waterproof; Stretches a little.

4. This is a model answer which demonstrates QWC, and would therefore score the full 6 marks: Plastics can be disposed of in three main ways: by putting them in landfill; by burning them; and by recycling them. Putting plastics into landfill wastes land and the plastics will remain there for a very long time as most plastics are not biodegradable, which means they do not decompose. Plastics can be burned in an incinerator, but this produces waste materials, harmful gases and toxic fumes. Recycling plastics is a better option, but they have to be sorted before recycling as different plastics cannot be recycled together and this can be difficult and time-consuming.

5. (a) Two layers of nylon; PTFE layer sandwiched between the nylon.
Your diagram should look similar to this:
Liquid water raindrop – too big to pass through fabric

Nylon outer layer

PTFE membrane   Nylon inner layer

Water vapour, perspiration – small enough to pass through holes in PTFE membrane

(b) The PTFE layer is too weak on its own – the nylon gives it strength.
(c) The pores in the fabric are too small to allow rainwater droplets through from the outside; The pores are large enough to let water vapour through to the outside from inside.

6. Any three from: Higher melting points; More rigid; Will not stretch.

7. Any four from: Nylon has strong bonds between the atoms in the molecules; They are very hard to break; Making it a strong material; The forces between the molecules are quite weak; When it is heated they weaken; The molecules can then slip over/past each other (enabling the material to be stretched and shaped).

Page 47

1. **Any two from:** New substances made; Change in mass; Heat taken in; Cannot be reversed.
2. To stop the food reacting with oxygen.
3. Eggs — Gives off carbon dioxide when cooked
   Emulsifier — Helps oil and water mix
   Baking powder — Good source of protein
   (2 marks if all correct, 1 mark if one line correct.)
4. **Any two from:** Improve taste; Stop it reacting with oxygen; Help it stay mixed together.
5. sodium hydrogencarbonate ⟶ sodium carbonate + water + carbon dioxide
6. Water-hating
7. **Any three from:** It gets softer; It breaks the cell walls; Releases the starch molecules; The starch molecules swell up.
8. The protein molecules change shape; They denature; The change is irreversible.
9. $2NaHCO_3 \longrightarrow Na_2CO_3 + H_2O + CO_2$ **(1 mark for correct formulae, 1 mark for balance.)**

Pages 48–49

1. Man-made/manufactured
2. **(a)** So that the molecules can travel easily to the nose.
   (b) So it is not washed off easily
3. alcohol + acid ⟶ ester + water
4. (b), (d), (a), (c) **or** (a), (b), (d), (c). **(2 marks for all correct, 1 mark if end with (c).)**
5. **(a)** Make sure they are safe to use.
   (b) (i) It has banned testing on animals.
   (ii) Any two from: They argue that it is cruel; They argue that animals do not have the same body chemistry as humans so the tests do not prove anything; On moral grounds; Religious beliefs.
6. A substance that dissolves in a liquid — Solvent
   A liquid that does the dissolving — Solution
   A mixture of a dissolved solid and a liquid — Solute
   (2 marks for all correct, 1 mark for one line correct.)
7. **(a)** Water
   (b) Propanone
8. As a solvent (**accept** as nail varnish remover).
9. The cosmetic has to be tested before use; They will argue that it will stop the cosmetic harming humans.
10. **(a)** It evaporates easily
    (b) Forces between ethyl ethanoate particles weaker; Forces between water particles stronger; Less energy needed to separate ethyl ethanoate particles than to separate water particles.
11. Forces between water particles strong; Forces between varnish particles strong; Interaction between water particles and varnish particles weak; The varnish particles do not separate and mix with the water particles.

Page 50

1. Solvent — Strong coloured material
   Colloid — Fine solid particles mixed in a liquid
   Binding medium — Liquid that dissolves substances
   Pigment — Oil that sticks to a surface
   (2 marks for all correct, 1 mark for one line correct.)
2. **(a)** To decorate it/protect it.
   (b) Water
3. Add a solvent to dissolve the oil.
4. The solvent evaporates (leaving behind the binding medium and pigment); The binding medium reacts with oxygen (from the air and goes hard) and this holds the pigment on the surface.
5. **(a)** They were radioactive.
   (b) Caused cancer amongst the people who used them.

C2: Chemical Resources

Pages 51–53

1.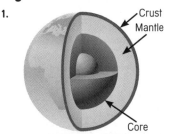
   Crust
   Mantle
   Core
   (1 mark for each correct label.)
2. **(a)** The core
   (b) The crust and the upper part of the mantle.
   (c) They have a lower density than the mantle.
3. The soil is very fertile.
4. **(a)** Volcanoes erupting; Earthquakes.
   (b) Plates moving apart increases the distance between the two shorelines.
   (c) There is lots of evidence to support it, e.g. fossils; It has been well tested by many scientists.
5. **(a)** Lava
   (b) Igneous
   (c) A cools fast – small crystals; **B** cools slow – big crystals.
   (d) Thick lava will cause violent eruptions; Runny lava leads to a much calmer volcano.
6. Lava — Area between crust and core of the Earth
   Mantle — Molten rock underground
   Magma — Molten rock above ground
   (2 marks for all correct, 1 mark for one correct.)
7. Convection currents **(1 mark)**; **And any one of:** Hot magma rises; Cold magma falls; Radioactive decay heats magma.
8. **This is a model answer, which demonstrates QWC, and would therefore score the full 6 marks:** Scientists tested Wegener's theory by using it to explain observations and found it to work. There is now a lot of other evidence to back up the theory. The discovery of the sea floor spreading where the plates are moving apart, with new rock forming in between, helped the theory to be accepted. Magnetic patterns in the rocks formed show that this has been happening for a long time. Other evidence, such as continents fitting together (e.g. South America and Africa) like a jigsaw, similar rocks on either side of the Atlantic, and similar species of animals on either side of the Atlantic, helped the theory to become accepted.
9. **(a)** The collision of an oceanic plate and a continental plate; The oceanic plate moves under the continental plate; Oceanic plate melts into the mantle.
   (b) Oceanic plates are more dense than continental plates.
10. Britain is not near a plate boundary, which is where most earthquakes occur.

Page 54

1. **(a)** Breaking up a substance using heat.
   (b) calcium carbonate ⟶ calcium oxide + carbon dioxide
2. **Any two from:** Noise – only work during day; Dust – spray water; Take up land – permission to mine granted by government; Changes shape of landscape – sympathetic, making good of any damage; Increase in traffic – improve roads and use only designated routes. **(1 mark for problem, 1 mark for reduction, 4 marks maximum.)**
3. **(a)** Between limestone and granite
   (b) Marble **or** granite; The others are too soft.
4. A material made from two or more different materials combined; To get the best of the properties of each.
5. Reinforced concrete has steel rods inside it; It has the strength and flexibility needed to make a bridge; Ordinary concrete would break.
6. Limestone is a sedimentary rock made from shells cemented together; Marble is metamorphic, made from limestone by heating and high pressure.

Page 55

1. A mixture of a metal with other elements (mainly metals).
2. Solder —————————— Joining electrical wires
   Brass ————————— Tooth fillings
   Amalgam ———×——— Musical instruments
   (2 marks for all correct, 1 mark for one correct.)
3. (a) **Any two of:** Copper ore is a finite resource; It needs lots of energy to extract from ore; Less energy is needed to recycle from scrap.
   (b) **Any one of:** Problems getting people to recycle rather than just throwing it away; Sorting out the copper from all the other materials.
4. Zinc; Brass is much harder than copper so it will not wear as much in purses and pockets.
5. (a) Copper atoms are changed into copper ions; By losing two electrons.
   (b) The impurities in the impure copper are left behind when the copper moves from the anode to the cathode; Only copper collects on the cathode.

Pages 56–57

1. Air/oxygen; Water
2.

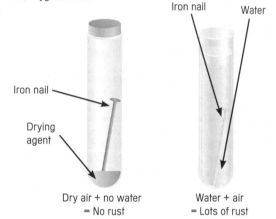

Iron nail   Water

Iron nail

Drying agent

Dry air + no water = No rust   Water + air = Lots of rust

(Diagram 1: 1 mark for sealed container, 1 mark for drying agent.)
(Diagram 2: 1 mark for container open to air, 1 mark for nail in contact with air and water.)
3. Stops contact with air/oxygen; Stops contact with water.
4. The oxide layer formed on exposure to air **(1 mark)**; protects the rest of the metal from any more contact with oxygen in the air **(1 mark)**.
5. It saves natural resources; It reduces disposal problems.
6. Sea water is salt water and salt water speeds up rusting; Washing stops the speeding up of rust by removing the salt.
7. (a) Use a magnet.
   (b) Iron is magnetic and aluminium is not.
8. (a) It is transparent
   (b) **Any one of:** Lightweight; Does not corrode; Rigid.
9. (a) **Any two from:** Steel has better properties than iron; It is stronger; Harder; Less likely to corrode.
   (b) iron + water + oxygen $\longrightarrow$ hydrated iron(III) oxide
10. Oxygen is added onto the iron/the iron loses electrons.
11. (a) Better fuel economy – because the car is lighter **(1 mark)**; The car lasts larger because the car will corrode less **(1 mark)**.
    (b) Aluminium is not as strong as steel.

Pages 58–59

1. (a) The air
   (b) The iron acts as a catalyst **(1 mark)**; speeding up the reaction **(1 mark)**.
   (c) The reaction goes forward and backwards **(1 mark)**; at the same time **(1 mark)**.
   (d) Manufacture of nitric acid; Fertilisers.
2. (a) 50%
   (b) The yield is reduced.

(c) **Any three from:** Catalyst; Energy; Wages; Plant; Plant maintenance; Raw materials; Rate at which the ammonia is made.
3. (a) Speeds it up.
   (b) Does not change the yield.
   (c) Increasing the pressure will increase the yield; Decreasing the pressure will reduce the yield.
   (d) Slows the reaction down.
4. Rate of reaction; Cost of energy; Cost of the equipment used to obtain the conditions.
5. $N_2 + 3H_2 \rightleftharpoons 2NH_3$ **(1 mark for correct formulae, 1 mark for balancing.)**
6. **Any two from:** The unreacted gases can be recycled; The reaction can be repeated many times; The ammonia is made quickly and so the daily amount produced is sufficient; The cost of producing the ammonia is as low as it can be.

Pages 60–61

1. (a) A solution containing H^+ ions/that turns litmus red/has a pH less than 7.
   (b) A soluble base/solution containing OH^- ions/that turns litmus blue/has a pH greater than 7.
   (c) acid + base $\longrightarrow$ salt + water
2. (a)

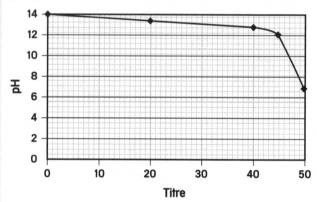

(1 mark for smooth curve, 1 mark for all five points plotted correctly, 1 mark for sensible axis, 1 mark for axes labelled.)
   (b) Blue
   (c) Green
   (d) Neutralisation
   (e) sodium hydroxide + sulfuric acid $\longrightarrow$ sodium sulfate + water
   (f) Nitric acid
3. sodium hydroxide, copper oxide, calcium carbonate **should be ringed (1 mark each)**.
4. (a) sodium hydroxide + hydrochloric acid $\longrightarrow$ sodium chloride + water
   (b) ammonia + nitric acid $\longrightarrow$ ammonium nitrate
   (c) calcium carbonate + nitric acid $\longrightarrow$ calcium nitrate + water + carbon dioxide
5. The pH scale.
6. Alkali × Hydrogen ions × OH^-(aq)
   Acid   Hydroxide ions H^+(aq)
   (2 marks for all correct, 1 mark for two lines correct.)
7. $H^+(aq) + OH^-(aq) \longrightarrow H_2O(l)$
8. (a) $NaOH + HCl \longrightarrow NaCl + H_2O$
   (b) $NH_3 + HNO_3 \longrightarrow NH_4NO_3$
   (c) $CaCO_3 + 2HNO_3 \longrightarrow Ca(NO_3)_2 + H_2O + CO_2$ **(1 mark for formulae, 1 mark for balancing.)**

Pages 62–63

1. (a) **N:** Nitrogen; **P:** Phosphorus; **K:** Potassium.
   (b) Plants need them to grow properly.
   (c) **Any one from:** To improve the yield; Grow bigger crops; Crops grow faster.
   (d) Chemical fertilisers can pollute water supplies, which leads to the death of aquatic organisms (eutrophication).

2. **(a)** **D** and **C**
    (b) **A** and **B**
    (c) **D** and **E**
3. **(a)** **Any one of:** Ammonium nitrate; Urea; Potassium nitrate.
    (b) Plants absorb fertilisers through their roots when the fertilisers have been dissolved in water.
4. Plants can take in nitrogen easily as a dissolved nitrate.
5. **(a)** Fertiliser will wash off the fields and run into the river; The fertiliser will help the algae to grow.
    (b) **Any four from:** Fish populations will fall; The algae blocks out light; Causing other plants to die; All the dead plant material will be decomposed by bacteria; That use up all the oxygen in the water; The fish need a good supply of oxygen to survive.
    (c) Eutrophication
6.

Ammonia solution

Burette containing sulfuric acid

Glass rod

Evaporating basin

Basin

Indicator paper

Glass rod

Ammonium sulfate in filter funnel

Bunsen burner

Measure amounts of acid and alkali; Add acid and test with indicator to make sure neutral; Evaporate and leave to crystallise; Filter to separate crystals. **(1 mark each from either text or diagram)**.

Pages 64–65

1. **Any one of:** As a flavouring; As a preservative.
2. Chlorine ⎯⎯⎯ Made in the solution during electrolysis of salt solution
    Sodium hydroxide ⎯⎯⎯ Made at the anode during electrolysis of salt solution
    Hydrogen ⎯⎯⎯ Made at the cathode during electrolysis of salt solution
    (2 marks for all correct, 1 mark for one or two correct.)
3. The products of the electrolysis are very reactive.
4. Chlorine bleaches moist litmus paper.
5. **(a)** Chlorine **and** sodium hydroxide
    (b) Sodium hydroxide
    (c) Hydrogen
    (d) Chlorine
6. **(a)** From sea water **(1 mark)**; mining rock salt **(1 mark)**; solution mining **(1 mark)**.
    (b) Subsidence
7. **(a)** **A:** Anode; **B:** Chlorine; **C:** Sodium hydroxide.
    (b) They would react with each other to make bleach.
8. **(a)** $2Cl^- \longrightarrow 2e^- + Cl_2$ **(1 mark for correct formulae, 1 mark for balance.)**
    (b) $2H^+ + 2e^- \longrightarrow H_2$ **(1 mark for correct formulae, 1 mark for balance.)**
9. **(a)** Reduction is the gain of electrons; Hydrogen gains electrons at the cathode.
    (b) Oxidation is the loss of electrons; Chloride ions lose electrons at the anode.

Physics

P1: Energy for the Home
Pages 66–68

1. joule/J
2. **(a)** Thermogram
    (b) Windows
3. **(a)** Helium; Highest specific heat capacity (SHC)
    (b) Energy = mass × SHC × change in temperature; Energy = 2 × 380 × 10; Energy = 7600 J. **(1 mark for calculation, 1 mark for correct answer.)**
4. The temperature stays the same; So the chocolate must be melting.
5. **(a)** Material **and** State change (solid to liquid/liquid to gas).
    (b) Energy = mass × specific latent heat; Energy = 20 × 330; Energy = 6600 J. **(1 mark for calculation, 1 mark for correct answer.)**
6. mass = energy ÷ (SHC × temperature change); mass = 660000 ÷ (440 × 15) = 100 kg **(1 mark for calculation, 1 mark for correct answer)**.
7. Temperature is a measurement of the average kinetic energy of particles; Heat is a measurement of energy on an absolute scale.
8. SHC = energy ÷ (mass × change in temperature); SHC = 7500 ÷ (0.5 × 6); SHC = 2500 J/kg°C. **(1 mark for calculation, 1 mark for correct answer.)**
9. **(a)** Break bonds; change state **(1 mark each)** but break intermolecular bonds **would get 2 marks**.
    (b) energy = mass × specific latent heat, rearrange to find SLH, SLH = energy ÷ mass, 66.8 ÷ 0.2 = 334 kJ/kg **(1 mark for calculation, 1 mark for correct answer)**.

Pages 69–71

1. **(a)** Infrared radiation is reflected by a dull or shiny surface.
    (b) Infrared radiation is absorbed by a rough surface.
2. **(a)** Cavity wall insulation
    (b) Loft insulation; Will take 6 months to save the original cost.
3. **(a)** 30,000 − 12,000 = 18,000 J
    (b) Efficiency = useful energy output ÷ total energy input; Efficiency = 18,000 ÷ 30,000; Efficiency = 0.6. (To put this into a percentage, multiply the answer by 100 = 60%). **(1 mark for calculation, 1 mark for correct answer.)**
    (c) It is less efficient than Jane's hairdryer (50% or 0.5 is lower than 0.6).
4. **(a)** Light bulb A: (11 ÷ 55) × 100 = 20%
    Light bulb B: (5 ÷ 50) × 100 = 10%
    Light bulb C: (18 ÷ 60) × 100 = 30%
    (2 marks for calculations)
    Light bulb C is most efficient. **(1 mark)**
    (b) 30% − 10% = 20%
5. **This is a model answer which demonstrates QWC, and would therefore score the full 6 marks:** Heat loss by conduction through windows can be reduced by installing double-glazing. The gap between the two panes of glass is filled with air, which is a good insulator. The narrow gap also reduces heat loss by convection. Heat loss through walls can be reduced by using cavity wall insulation. Insulation material is placed inside a gap in the wall, which reduces the heat loss. Fibreglass loft insulation works in a similar way to cavity wall insulation, trapping layers of air between the fibres and reducing heat loss by conduction and convection. Shiny foil can be placed on walls behind radiators to reflect heat energy back into the room.
6. Conduction: Transfer of KE; Between particles (including free electrons).
    Convection: Expansion when a liquid or gas is heated; Causes a decrease in density which results in fluid flow.
    Radiation: Infrared radiation is an electromagnetic wave; Needs no medium.
7. Useful energy = 64 J a second, wastes 16 J a second **(1 mark)**, 16 × 60 × 60 **(1 mark)** = 57.6 kJ wasted in an hour **(1 mark)**.

Page 72

1. (a) **A:** peak; **B:** trough; **C:** amplitude; **D:** wavelength.
   (b) Frequency = 120 waves ÷ 30 seconds; Frequency = 4 Hz.
   (1 mark for calculation, 1 mark for correct answer.)
   (c) Wave speed = frequency × wavelength, 4 × 50 = 200 m/s
   (1 mark for calculation, 1 mark for correct answer).
2. Microwave; Infrared; Visible light; Ultraviolet; X-rays
3. Wavelength = speed ÷ frequency; Wavelength = 330 ÷ 194; Wavelength = 1.70 m. **(1 mark for calculation, 1 mark for correct answer.)**

Page 73

1. **Any two from:** Light turned on and off; Produce short and long pulses; Different combinations of pulses code for different letters.
2. (a) (i) **B**
       (ii) **C**
3. Pits store digital information; Laser/light shone onto surface of CD; Light reflected from pits; Reflected pulses converted into (electrical) signal.

Pages 74–75

1. (a) Water **and** fat
   (b) About 1 cm
   (c) Infrared
2. (a) Mobile phone masts use microwave radiation; Which may be harmful to humans; Although there is no proven link between health problems and mobile phone masts.
   (b) Check the results; Of published scientific studies into the health effects of mobile phone masts.
3. (a) Large obstacles in the way (i.e. trees/mountains); Poor weather conditions; Curvature of Earth; Interference between signals.
   (b) Reduce distance between transmitters; Put masts on hills/ high buildings.
4. Most of the microwaves are absorbed by water and fat particles; In the outer layers of the food; Increasing their kinetic energy; Some microwaves may pass to the middle of the food and be absorbed; Or kinetic energy is transferred from the outer layers to the centre by conduction or convection.

Pages 76–77

1. **Any two from:** Remote controls; Automatic door sensors; Burglar alarms; Security lights; Computer data links; Cooking
2. (a) (i) A is a digital signal, B is an analogue signal. **(1 mark)**.
       (ii) Digital signal is on or off; Analogue signal is continuous.
   (b) Digital; Digital signals have only two states (on or off) so are therefore less susceptible to noise.
   (c) 0010010101
3. (a) Two or more signals sent down an optical fibre at the same time/simultaneously.
   (b) **Any two from:** More data sent simultaneously; Multiple users; Faster transmission.

Pages 78–79

1. (a) **Any two from:** Radios; Mobile phones; Laptops (wireless internet); Remote controls.
   (b) **Any two from:** Signals available 24 hours a day; No wiring needed so available in remote places; Portable.
2. Anyone with a DAB radio can receive digital radio. [✗]
   DAB radios can receive digital broadcasts and old analogue signals. [✓]
   There are far more digital stations available than analogue stations. [✓]
   Digital signals sometimes contain more interference than analogue signals. [✗]
3. (a) Both radio stations are transmitting on a similar frequency so their analogue signals; Are interfering with each other, leading to poor reception.
   (b) **Any one of:** One station changes its frequency; Either station switches to digital transmission.
4. Long wave signals; reflected by the ionosphere/back to Earth (around the curve of the Earth).

5. (a) Longwave signals diffracted by hill; Changes direction and reaches radio antenna; Shorter wavelength signal not diffracted.
   (b) Diffraction causes wave to spread out which results in some signal loss; Interference caused by signal reflected by hills.

Pages 80–81

1. (a) Seismometer
   (b) **Any three from:** P-waves are longitudinal; Faster than s-waves; Can travel through solids and liquids; **S-waves** are transverse; Slower than p-waves so arrive after p-waves at seismometer; Can only travel through solids.
2. (a) Cause sunburn/skin cancer
   (b) Sun Protection Factor
   (c) Safe time = time without sun block × SPF; 3 × 20 = 60 minutes; 10 × 20 = 200 minutes; 25 × 20 = 500 minutes. **(1 mark for each correct answer.)**
3. Scientists repeated their measurements with new equipment; Different scientists also repeated the same measurements and found the same results.
4. S-waves are transverse so; Cannot pass through liquid; Shadow zone shows; Outer core is liquid.
5. Hole in ozone layer shows human activities (use of CFCs) reducing ozone levels; Ozone absorbs UV radiation; Continued use of CFCs could lead to holes developing over populated areas; Hugely increasing risk of skin cancer due to increased exposure to UV radiation; International agreement on banning CFCs to prevent this.

P2: Living for the Future (Energy Resources)
Pages 82–83

1. (a) Light
   (b) Increase surface area; More light captured; Higher electrical energy output.
   (c) **Any three from:** Radiation absorbed and transferred to heat energy; Produces convection currents to drive wind turbines; Passive solar heating using glass; Reflected to a focus by a mirror.
2. (a) **Any three from:** Low maintenance; No need for fuel; Long life; No polluting waste; Reduce energy costs.
   (b) Best position for the panel to absorb maximum sunlight; No power at night or in bad weather so need to have other sources of electricity.
3. **Advantages:** Renewable; No polluting waste; Doesn't contribute to the greenhouse effect and global warming.
   Disadvantages: Dependent on wind speed so not a constant supply – must have a back-up power-generating source; Visual pollution.
4. (a) Increased distance from light source decreases light intensity; So decreases output.
   (b) Surface exposed could also affect the output.
   (c) **Any six from:** Passive solar heating: Glass is transparent so Sun's radiation passes through it; Heated surfaces emit infrared radiation of longer wavelength; Glass reflects this longer wavelength infrared so inside of building warms up. Photocell: Energy from Sun absorbed by photocell; Electrons are knocked loose from the silicon atoms in the crystal; Electrons flow freely.

Pages 84–85

1. (a) Moving a magnet; Within a coil of wire.
   (b) **Any two from:** Move the magnet more quickly; Use a stronger magnet; Increase the number of turns on the coil of wire.
2. (a) Alternating current; Electric charge is reversing direction.
   (b) A generator
3. Heats water – steam produced – turns turbine – turns generator. **(All four correct, 2 marks; two or three correct, 1 mark.)**
4. Efficiency = useful output ÷ total input (× 100); Efficiency = 3 MW ÷ 12 MW; Efficiency = 0.25 (or × 100 = 25%). **(1 mark for calculation, 1 mark for correct answer.)**
5. 125,000 J useful energy out = 25% of total in; Total input = 4 × 125,000 J; Input = 500,000 J. **(2 marks for calculation, 1 mark for correct answer.)**

Pages 86–87

1. **Supports:** Atmospheric carbon dioxide levels are rising due to human activity; Increased carbon dioxide levels leads to global warming from the greenhouse effect.
    Refutes: Solar radiation reaching the Earth has increased at the same time as the temperature has increased; Humans don't affect solar radiation.
2. Cutting down large numbers of trees; Less carbon dioxide taken from the atmosphere by the photosynthesis of trees; Increased carbon dioxide levels lead to global warming.
3. **Any two from:** Methane; Carbon dioxide; Water vapour; Nitrous oxide; Ozone.
4. **This is a model answer, which demonstrates QWC, and would therefore score the full 6 marks:** The greenhouse effect is a scientific process that can be observed and experimented on so it's easy for scientists to agree on it. Scientists can't agree on human activity affecting global warming as it's a very complex issue that is not fully understood. The number of interacting factors that affect global warming mean it's very difficult to isolate one factor (human activity) and categorically state that it is having an effect. While there is a large amount of evidence that supports the idea that human activity is leading to global warming there is other evidence that refutes this idea.
5. (a) The global temperature increased steadily up until 1940; It then decreased at a similar rate for the next 20 years; It then rose again up to 2000.
    (b) 0.4°C (**Accept** 0.3°C **or** 0.5°C)

Pages 88–89

1.

Type of fuel used in power stations	Example of fuel	Advantage	Disadvantage
Fossil fuels	Coal/oil/ gas	Reliable	Will run out/ produces carbon dioxide that leads to global warming.
Renewable biomass	Manure/ straw/ wood	Renewable so won't run out.	Still produce some carbon dioxide that leads to global warming.
Nuclear fuels	Uranium/ plutonium	Reliable, produces very little carbon dioxide.	Fuel and waste is very dangerous, high cost in disposing of waste.

(2 marks for each correct row.)

2. Power = current × voltage (P = I × V); P = 10 × 230; P = 2300 W. **(1 mark for calculation, 1 mark for correct answer.)**
3. (a) Power rating of device ÷ time appliance used for in hours.
    (b) Cost = units × cost per unit; Cost = 4 × 10; Cost = 40 pence.
        (1 mark for calculation, 1 mark for correct answer.)
4. (a)

Appliance	Power rating in kilowatts	Average time used each week (hours)	Total energy used in a week (kWh)
Hairdryer	2.3	1	**2.3**
Dishwasher	1.2	**2.5**	3
Washing machine	**1.7**	4	6.8
TV	0.12	**10**	1.2

(b) Power = 2.3 KW = 2300 W
    Power = current × voltage
    Current = power ÷ voltage
    Current = 2300 ÷ 230
    Current = 10 A
    (1 mark for calculation, 1 mark for correct answer.)
5. **Advantages:** Less demand at night; Cheaper; Avoids wasting electricity.
    Disadvantages: Appliances such as washing machines noisy to run at night.
6. Heating large amounts of cables in the national grid would lead to a large amount of energy wasted; The national grid solves this problem by increasing the voltage; This decreases the current; So lowers the temperature of wires, so less energy wasted as heat.

Pages 90–91

1. Protective clothing; Use shielding (i.e. lead apron); Keep distance between her and substance as great as possible; Keep exposure time to a minimum.
2. **Alpha:** Smoke detectors.
    Beta: Any one from: Tracers; Paper thickness gauges.
    Gamma: Any one from: Treating cancer; Tracers; Non-destructive testing; Sterilising equipment.
3. (a) A few mm aluminium
    (b) Alpha
    (c) Gamma
4. Gamma
5. **Positive ions:** When electrons are lost from atoms.
    Negative ions: When electrons are gained by atoms.
6. (a) Plutonium
    (b) **Low level:** sealed in canisters and stored/buried in landfill.
        High level: encased in glass and stored underground.
7. (a) **1** = Beta; stopped by thin sheet of aluminium; **2** = Gamma; only stopped by lead; **3** = Alpha; stopped by paper.
    (b) Carry out repeat experiments.

Pages 92–93

1. Planet, star, galaxy. **(1 mark for each correct label and 1 mark for the correct order.)**
2. A light year is the distance light travels in one year.
3. (a) An unmanned probe; Temperature and atmospheric conditions; Would make it very hostile and dangerous for humans.
    (b) Due to the large distance between Earth and Venus; Data would be sent back from planet; As the Moon is much closer to Earth; Actual samples could be sent back.
4.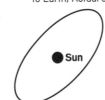
5. The gravitational attraction; Of the Sun.
6. **Any two from:** Kilometres used for distances within the solar system; Light years used for distances between solar systems; Across our galaxy; Between galaxies.

Pages 94–95

1. (a) Asteroid is made of rocks; **Any one of:** Comet is made from and ice and dust; Has a tail formed from trail of debris.
    (b) Craters; Sudden change in the fossil record; Unusual chemical elements in the rocks.
    (c) Iron cores merge to form the core of the Earth; Less dense material orbits and forms the Moon.
2. (a) Near Earth Object
    (b) They may be on a collision course with Earth.
3. Jupiter's large gravity; Pulls them apart.

4. The further from the Sun, the slower the comet; As the comet gets closer to the Sun its speed increases; Due to the gravitational attraction of the Sun.

5. Survey the skies using telescopes; Monitor object's progress (trajectory); Could deflect object.

6. Samples from the Moon's surface indicate it was once molten; Moon's small iron core; Similar collisions occur in other star systems.

Pages 96–97

1. (a) **Any two from:** Formed billions of years ago; Huge explosion; Universe still expanding.
   (b) All galaxies moving away from us (universe expanding); Distant galaxies are moving away from us faster; Detect microwave radiation from all parts of the universe.

2. (a) Gravity
   (b) Hydrogen

3. Star shrinks rapidly, then explodes to form a supernova; The remnants of the star form a neutron star; A black hole is left behind.

4. (a) **Any two from:** The church was very influential and believed that the Earth was the centre of the universe; The Sun seems to move across the sky; Technology had not progressed sufficiently to make good observations.
   (b) **Any two from:** Venus did not move smoothly across sky; Retrograde motion; Orbit of planets not solely due to rotation of Earth.

5. (a) Light from galaxies moving away from us; Is further towards the red end of the visible spectrum than expected.
   (b) Light from distant galaxies; Much more red-shifted.
   (c) The fate of the universe

1. Label the diagram of the Earth's structure. [3]

2. **(a)** Name the part of the Earth's structure that is made mostly of iron. _____ [1]

    (b) What is the **lithosphere**? [1]

    _____

    (c) Explain why tectonic plates are found on top of the Earth's mantle. [1]

    _____

3. Why do some people choose to live on the slopes of active volcanoes? [1]

    _____

4. The diagram shows various tectonic plates around the Atlantic Ocean. The lines show the location of the boundaries between the plates.

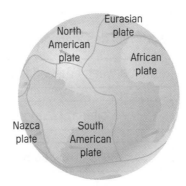

    (a) What **two** events are more likely to occur along the boundaries of the plates? [2]

    _____ **and** _____

    (b) Explain why the distance between the UK and America is increasing. [1]

    _____

    (c) Explain why scientists have come to accept plate tectonic theory. [2]

    _____

    _____

5. The diagram shows a geological section of a volcano.

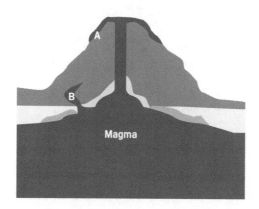

(a) Name the molten rock found at **A** when the volcano erupts. .... [1]

(b) Name the type of rock made at **A** and **B** when the molten rock cools down. .... [1]

(c) Describe how the rocks at **A** and **B** will differ in appearance. Why are they different? [2]

....

....

(d) Explain what causes some volcanoes to erupt violently while others simply leak molten rock. [2]

....

....

6. Draw a line to link each word with its correct description. [2]

Lava	Area between crust and core of the Earth
Mantle	Molten rock underground
Magma	Molten rock above ground

[Total: .... / 20]

Higher Tier

7. Describe the process that causes movement in the mantle. [2]

....

....

8. When Wegener first published his tectonic plate theory in 1914, it was not accepted by scientists. Explain what must happen for a theory to be accepted and describe how a discovery in the 1960s and other evidence backed up Wegener's theory.

   🖉 *The quality of your written communication will be assessed in this question.* [6]

   ....

   ....

   ....

   ....

   ....

   ....

   ....

   ....

   ....

   ....

   ....

9. **(a)** Describe the process of **subduction**. [3]

   ....

   ....

   ....

   (b) Why do oceanic plates move under continental plates when the two collide? [1]

   ....

10. Explain why earthquakes are not very common in Britain. [1]

   ....

   ....

   [Total: .... / 13]

1. (a) What is **thermal decomposition?** [1]

_____

(b) Write the **word** equation for the thermal decomposition of limestone (calcium carbonate). [1]

_____

2. There are disadvantages to living next door to a mine. Pick **two** disadvantages and explain how they can be minimised. [4]

_____

_____

_____

3. Look at the following rocks, which are in order of hardness, starting with the softest.

clay   limestone   granite

(a) Suggest where marble would go in the order. _____ [1]

(b) Choose **one** material from the list you would use for floor tiles and explain why. [2]

_____

4. What is a composite material? [2]

_____

[Total: _____ / 11]

Higher Tier

5. Explain why reinforced concrete is better than just concrete for making bridges. [3]

_____

_____

6. Limestone and marble are both forms of calcium carbonate. Describe how their formation has made them into different rocks. [2]

_____

_____

_____

[Total: _____ / 5]

1. What is an alloy? _____ [1]

2. Draw a line to link the alloy with **one** of its main uses. [2]

Solder		Joining electrical wires
Brass		Tooth fillings
Amalgam		Musical instruments

3. **(a)** Explain why it is important to recycle copper scrap. [2]

_____

_____

(b) Describe **one** difficulty in recycling copper. [1]

_____

4. Name the metal that is mixed with copper to make brass and explain why coins are made from brass rather than copper. [2]

_____

_____

[Total: _____ / 8]

Higher Tier

5. The copper that is used for electrical wiring has to be very pure. Pure copper can be obtained by electrolysis, using copper(II) sulfate solution as the electrolyte.

   (a) Describe in detail the process taking place at the **positive** electrode (anode) during the electrolysis of impure copper. [2]

   _____

   _____

   (b) Explain as fully as you can how this process produces pure copper from impure copper. [2]

   _____

   _____

   [Total: _____ / 4]

1. Name the **two** substances that must be in contact with an iron nail before it will rust. [2]

_____ **and** _____

2. Outline an experiment you would use to show that an iron nail will not rust in dry air but will rust in wet air. Use diagrams in your answer. [4]

3. Explain how painting a car protects the steel underneath from rusting. [2]

_____

_____

4. Aluminium is more reactive than iron. Explain why it does not corrode. [2]

_____

_____

5. A new law in the UK states that 95% of the materials in a car must be able to be recycled from 2015 onwards. Why do you think that this law has been passed? [2]

_____

_____

6. Explain why it is a good idea to wash the underside of your car if you have driven through sea water. [2]

_____

_____

7. (a) Suggest a quick way of separating scrap aluminium and scrap steel. [1]

(b) Explain how your method works. [1]

8. On a modern car…

(a) Suggest why glass is used to make the windscreen. [1]

(b) Suggest why plastic is used to make the bumpers and trims. [1]

9. (a) Steel is an alloy composed mainly of iron. Why is steel more useful than iron? [2]

(b) Write the **word** equation for rusting. [1]

10. Rusting is an example of an oxidation reaction. Explain why it is this type of reaction. [1]

[Total: .... / 22]

Higher Tier

11. (a) Why is it better to use aluminium to make the body of a car rather than steel? Link the **advantage** to a property of aluminium. [2]

(b) What would be the main **disadvantage**? [1]

[Total: .... / 3]

1. **(a)** The Haber process is used to make ammonia. Where is the raw material nitrogen obtained from? [1]

_____

(b) Explain why the nitrogen and hydrogen is passed over iron. [2]

_____

(c) The production of ammonia is an example of a reversible reaction. Explain what this means. [2]

_____

(d) State **two** uses of the ammonia made in the Haber process. [2]

_____ **and** _____

2. Look at the following graph. It shows how the yield of the Haber process changes with different conditions. Use the graph to help you answer the following questions.

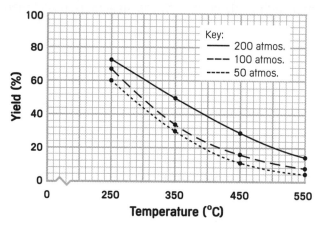

(a) Write down the yield at 200 atmospheres pressure and a temperature of 350°C. _____ [1]

(b) Describe what happens to the yield as the temperature is increased. [1]

_____

(c) Describe **three** costs that are involved in making ammonia in the Haber process. [3]

_____

_____

_____

[Total: _____ **/ 12]**

3. This question is about the conditions used in the Haber process.

(a) Explain how using a catalyst affects the rate of the reaction. [1]

_____

(b) Explain how using a catalyst affects the yield of the reaction. [1]

_____

(c) Use the graph on page 25 to outline how changing the pressure of the reaction changes the yield of ammonia. [2]

_____

_____

(d) Describe the **disadvantage** of reducing the temperature of the reaction. [1]

_____

4. Explain what the **three** main considerations are when choosing the optimum conditions for an industrial process. [3]

_____

_____

_____

5. Write the balanced **symbol** equation for the reaction of nitrogen and hydrogen to make ammonia in the Haber process. [2]

_____

6. Explain why a relatively low yield is acceptable in the Haber process. [2]

_____

_____

[Total: _____ **/ 12]**

C2 Acids and Bases

1. **(a)** What is an acid? [1]

    ....

    (b) What is an alkali? [1]

    ....

    (c) Complete the general equation. [1]

    acid + base ⟶ .... + ...

2. A beaker containing 100 cm³ of sodium hydroxide has universal indicator solution added to it. Sulfuric acid is then added using a burette and the pH of the solution is estimated by gauging the colour of the liquid. The solution was constantly stirred. The results are shown below.

Volume of acid added (cm³)	pH of solution
0	14.0
20	13.5
40	12.8
45	12.0
50	7.0

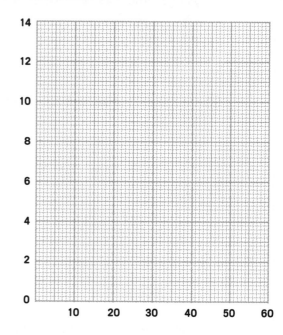

    (a) Plot a graph of the results on the graph paper. [4]

    (b) Suggest what colour the solution was at the start. .... [1]

    (c) Suggest what colour the solution was at the end. .... [1]

    (d) What is the name given to this type of reaction? .... [1]

    (e) Complete the **word** equation for the reaction taking place. [1]

    sodium hydroxide + sulfuric acid ⟶ .... + ...

    (f) Suggest which acid you would use to make sodium nitrate. [1]

    ....

3. (Ring) **three** substances from the list that will neutralise sulfuric acid.　　　[3]

    sodium hydroxide　　　**water**　　　**sodium chloride**　　　**copper oxide**　　　**calcium carbonate**
    　　　sulfur　　　**hydrogen**　　　**nitric acid**　　　**universal indicator**

4. Complete the following **word** equations.

    (a) sodium hydroxide + hydrochloric acid ⟶ _____ + _____　　　[1]

    (b) ammonia + nitric acid ⟶ _____　　　[1]

    (c) calcium carbonate + nitric acid ⟶ _____ + _____ + _____　　　[1]

5. What measurement scale is used to show the concentration of hydrogen ions in an acid?　　　[1]

    _____

6. Draw lines between the boxes to link them correctly.　　　[2]

Alkali		Hydrogen ions		$OH^-(aq)$
Acid		Hydroxide ions		$H^+(aq)$

    [Total: _____ / 21]

    Higher Tier

    7. Complete the ionic equation that describes neutralisation.　　　[1]

        _____ + _____ ⟶ H_2O

    8. Write balanced **symbol** equations for the **three** reactions in **Q4**.

        (a) _____　　　[1]

        (b) _____　　　[1]

        (c) _____　　　[2]

        [Total: _____ / 5]

1. This is the label on a bag of fertiliser.

   Contents
   N (20%) **P** (10%) **K** (10%)

   (a) What do the letters **N**, **P** and **K** stand for? [3]

   _____

   (b) Why are they put in fertilisers? [1]

   _____

   (c) Why do farmers use fertilisers? [1]

   _____

   (d) Give **one** argument against using chemical fertilisers. [1]

   _____

2. Look at the **five** reactants used to make fertilisers.

   A Nitric acid   **B** Potassium hydroxide

   C Sulfuric acid   **D** Ammonia

   E Phosphoric acid

   Select which **two** reactants you would use to make each of the following fertilisers. Write the letter in each box.

	Reagent 1	Reagent 2	
(a) Ammonium sulfate	◯	◯	[2]
(b) Potassium nitrate	◯	◯	[2]
(c) Ammonium phosphate	◯	◯	[2]

3. **(a)** Ammonium sulfate and ammonium phosphate are both fertilisers that contain nitrogen. [1]

   Name another fertiliser that contains nitrogen. _____

   (b) Explain why fertilisers must be soluble in water. [1]

   _____

4. Explain why it is important for fertilisers to provide nitrogen in the form of soluble nitrates. [1]

_____

[Total: .... / 15]

Higher Tier

5. The diagram shows an arable (crop-growing) farm. The farm is intensively farmed and the farmer uses a lot of fertiliser to increase his yields.

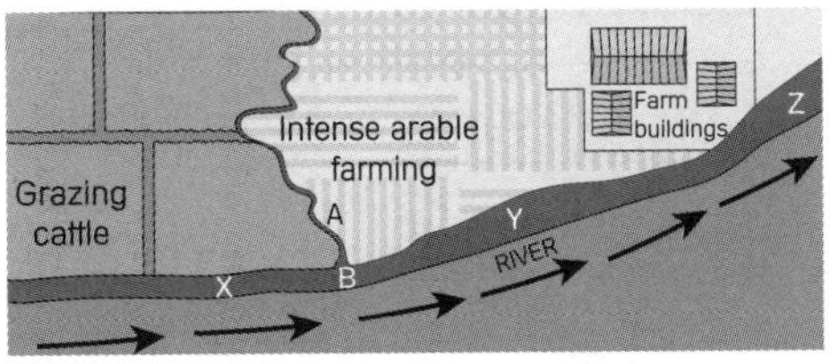

Water from the farm drains into the stream labelled **A**. This then drains into the River Lonsdale at **B** (which flows from left to right). The river has an abundance of fish at **X**, however, anglers are increasingly complaining about the lack of fish at **Z**.

(a) Explain why you would find a lot of growth of simple algae at **Y**. [2]

_____

_____

(b) Explain how this growth of simple algae can eventually affect the population of fish in the river. [4]

_____

_____

_____

_____

(c) What is the name given to the process described above? _____ [1]

6. Describe in detail, including diagrams, the method you would use to make a pure, dry sample of ammonium sulfate from ammonia solution and sulfuric acid. [4]

[Total: .... / 11]

1. Describe **one** use of solid sodium chloride in the home. [1]

2. Draw lines between the boxes to match each substance with the method used to obtain it. [2]

Chlorine	Made in the solution during electrolysis of salt solution
Sodium hydroxide	Made at the anode during electrolysis of salt solution
Hydrogen	Made at the cathode during electrolysis of salt solution

3. Explain why the electrodes must be inert in the electrolysis of sodium chloride solution. [1]

4. Describe what effect chlorine has on moist litmus paper. [1]

5. **(a)** Name the **two** products of the electrolysis of sodium chloride that are reacted together to make household bleach. [1]

_____ **and** _____

(b) Name the product of the electrolysis of sodium chloride that is used to make soap. [1]

(c) Name the product of the electrolysis of sodium chloride that is used to make margarine. [1]

(d) Name the product of the electrolysis of sodium chloride that is used to make PVC. [1]

6. **(a)** Describe **three** methods of extracting sodium chloride in the UK. [3]

(b) Suggest a problem caused by salt mining in Cheshire. [1]

7. Look at the diagram of a sodium chloride electrolysis cell.

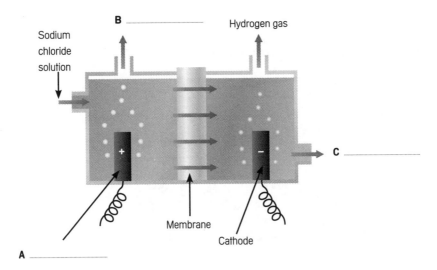

(a) Label part A and substances B and C on the diagram. [3]

(b) Why is it important to keep chlorine and sodium hydroxide apart when they have been made? [1]

[Total: .... / 17]

8. Write down the balanced half-equations for the reactions that happen at each electrode during the electrolysis of sodium chloride solution.

(a) At the anode .... [2]

(b) At the cathode .... [2]

9. (a) What is a reduction reaction and at which electrode will this occur during the electrolysis of sodium chloride solution? [2]

(b) What is an oxidation reaction and at which electrode will this occur during the electrolysis of sodium chloride solution? [2]

[Total: .... / 8]

1. The unit used to measure temperature is degrees Celsius (°C). What is the unit of **energy**?   [1]

    _____

2. This image uses colour to represent temperature.

    Blue

    Red

    Yellow/white

    (a) Name this type of image.   [1]

    _____

    (b) From where is the house losing the most heat energy?   [1]

    _____

3. Look at the table of data.

Material	Specific heat capacity (J/kg°C)
Copper	380
Aluminium	880
Water	4200
Titanium	523
Silver	233
Helium	5193

    (a) Which material will require the most energy to raise its temperature by 1°C? Explain your answer.   [2]

    _____

    _____

    (b) Calculate the energy needed to raise the temperature of 2 kg of copper by 10°C.   [2]

    _____

    _____

    _____

4. Julie heated some chocolate. She measured the temperature regularly and plotted her results on the graph below.

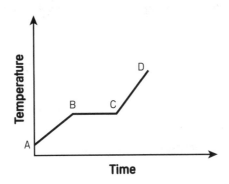

Explain what is happening to the chocolate between points **B** and **C**. [2]

....

....

5. The amount of energy needed to melt or boil a material is called the **specific latent heat**.

(a) What **two** factors does a material's specific latent heat depend on? [2]

.... **and** ....

(b) The specific latent heat of ice is 330 J/g. How much energy is required to melt 20 g of ice? [2]

....

....

[Total: .... / 13]

Higher Tier

6. The specific heat capacity of iron is 440 J/kg°C. On a sunny day a section of railway track heats up from 10°C to 25°C. This requires 660 kJ of energy. What is the mass of the railway track? [2]

....

....

....

7. Distinguish between temperature and heat. [2]

....

....

8. Harry carries out an experiment using 0.5 kg of paraffin wax. It takes 7500 J of energy to raise the temperature by 6°C. Calculate the specific heat capacity of paraffin wax. [2]

9. Sadiq heats 200 g of ice. The graph shows his data.

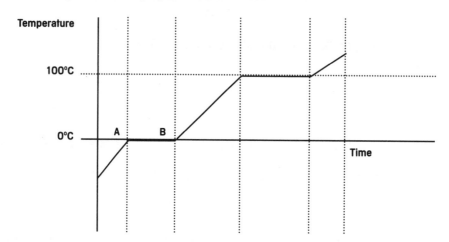

(a) Energy is supplied between points **A** and **B**. Explain why the temperature of the water does not change. [2]

(b) The energy required to melt this ice is 66.8 kJ. Use this information to calculate the specific latent heat capacity of melting water. [2]

[Total: .... / 10]

1. Describe what happens to infrared radiation when it comes into contact with

(a) a shiny surface. .... [1]

(b) a dull or rough surface. .... [1]

2. The table below shows the initial cost and annual saving on energy bills of three different energy-saving methods.

Method	Initial cost £	Annual saving on energy bills £
Double-glazing	3000	200
Loft insulation	200	400
Cavity wall insulation	1000	500

(a) Which of the above methods reduces heat loss by the most in a year? [1]

....

(b) Explain which of the above methods has the shortest payback time. [2]

....

....

....

3. Jane uses a hairdryer. Some of the energy is wasted as sound. The sankey diagram shows the total energy input and the output energies.

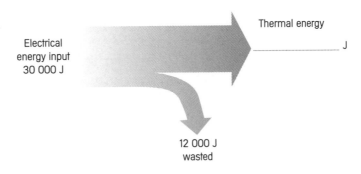

Electrical energy input 30 000 J

Thermal energy .... J

12 000 J wasted

(a) Calculate the thermal energy output. [1]

....

....

(b) Calculate the efficiency of the hairdryer. [2]

....

....

(c) A different hairdryer has an efficiency of 50%. Is this more or less efficient than Jane's hairdryer?   [1]

4. **(a)** Light bulb A uses 55 J of energy per second and gives out 11 J of light energy. Light bulb B uses 50 J of energy per second and gives out 5 J of light energy. Light bulb C uses 60 J of energy per second and gives out 18 J of light energy. Which light bulb is the most efficient?   [3]

(b) What is the difference in efficiency between the most and least efficient light bulbs?   [1]

5. Explain how the design features of a home can help to prevent heat loss.   [6]

✏ *The quality of your written communication will be assessed in this question.*

[Total: .... / 19]

6. Name and describe the **three** ways energy is transferred. [6]

....

....

....

....

....

7. A light bulb has an efficiency of 80% and a total energy input of 80 J per second. How much energy does the light bulb waste in an hour? [3]

....

....

....

[Total: .... / 9]

1. Look at the diagram of a wave.

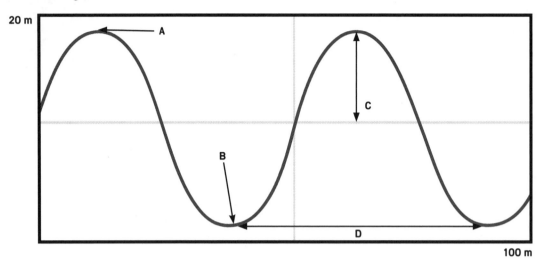

(a) Write down the correct name for each of the features labelled on the diagram of a wave. [4]

A .... B .... C .... D ....

(b) James counts the number of waves which pass a point in 30 seconds. James counts 120 waves. Calculate the frequency of the wave. [2]

....

....

(c) Calculate the wave speed of the wave shown above. [2]

....

....

2. Fill in the blanks below to show the types of electromagnetic waves that make up the spectrum. [5]

radio waves ....

.... **gamma**

[Total: .... / 13]

Higher Tier

3. The speed of sound in air is measured to be 330 m/s. Calculate the wavelength of a sound wave which has a frequency of 194 Hz. [2]

....

....

[Total: .... / 2]

1. Morse code can be used to send signals. How is light used to send a message using Morse code? [2]

_____

_____

2. The diagrams below show what can happen to a ray of light when it is incident on a glass-air boundary.

A

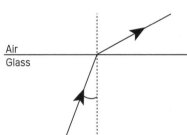

B

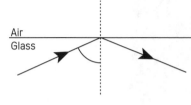

C

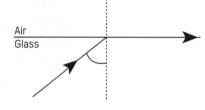

(a) Which picture, **A, B** or **C**, shows what will happen to the light when,

    (i) the angle of incidence is **greater than** the critical angle? [1]

_____

    (ii) the angle of incidence is **equal to** the critical angle? [1]

_____

[Total: _____ / 4]

Higher Tier

3. Describe how data is stored on a compact disc and how this data is read by a laser. [4]

_____

_____

_____

_____

[Total: _____ / 4]

1. Microwaves are part of the electromagnetic spectrum. Microwaves can be used to cook food.

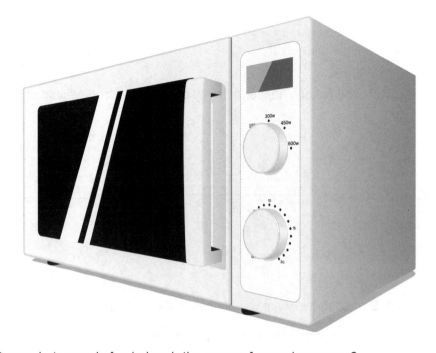

(a) Which **two** substances in food absorb the energy from microwaves? [2]

_____ **and** _____

(b) Approximately how far do microwaves penetrate into the food? [1]

_____

(c) Which other part of the electromagnetic spectrum is often used to cook food? [1]

_____

2. **(a)** A large mobile phone mast is being built near a group of houses. Some of the residents are worried about this while others don't think it's a problem.
Explain why the residents have these two different viewpoints. [3]

_____

_____

_____

(b) What evidence could the residents use to help them form an opinion on the safety of the phone mast? [2]

_____

_____

[Total: _____ / 9]

3. Microwaves can be used to transmit signals.

(a) Some houses are unable to receive mobile phone signals. Describe the conditions that will affect a microwave signal. [4]

....

....

....

....

(b) Describe **two** ways in which these problems can be reduced. [2]

....

....

4. A common misconception is that microwave ovens cook food 'from the inside out.' Explain why this is not the case. [5]

....

....

....

....

....

[Total: .... / 11]

1. Infrared is a type of electromagnetic radiation. Write down **two** uses of infrared radiation. [2]

    .... **and** ....

2. These pictures show signals.

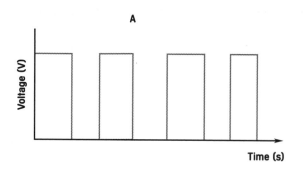

    A ....   B ....

    (a) (i) Label the signals. [1]

    (ii) How did you come to this conclusion? [2]

    ....

    ....

    (b) Which of the above signals could noise be most effectively removed from and why? [2]

    ....

    ....

    (c) The diagram shows a signal. Write the code for this signal in the boxes below. [1]

    [Total: .... / 8]

3. Multiplexing can be used to send digital signals.

(a) What is multiplexing? [1]

....

....

(b) State **two** benefits of multiplexing. [2]

....

....

....

[Total: .... / 3]

1. Many modern devices use wireless technology.

    (a) Write down **two** uses of wireless technology. [2]

    ....

    ....

    (b) Write down **two** benefits of wireless technology. [2]

    ....

    ....

2. Simon is writing about DAB radio.

    Put a tick (✓) next to each of the statements that are correct and a cross (✗) next to each of the
    statements that are wrong. [4]

    Anyone with a DAB radio can receive digital radio. ☐

    DAB radios can receive digital broadcasts and old analogue signals. ☐

    There are far more digital stations available than analogue stations. ☐

    Digital signals sometimes contain more interference than analogue signals. ☐

3. Listeners of a radio station have been complaining of poor reception. Another local station, F-FM,
    transmits on a very similar frequency.

    (a) Explain the cause of the poor reception. [2]

    ....

    ....

    (b) Give a possible solution. [1]

    ....

    [Total: .... / 11]

4. Radio signals from France are often heard on the South coast of England. Describe how the ionosphere enables these signals to be transmitted around the curve of the Earth. [2]

....

....

....

5. Look at the house in the picture. This house is able to receive analogue radio broadcasts.

(a) Explain why it cannot receive shorter wave signals such as digital radio or mobile phone signals. [3]

....

....

....

(b) Suggest why the analogue signal will not be as clear as an analogue signal received on top of the hill. [2]

....

....

....

[Total: .... / 7]

1. This question is about seismic waves.

    (a) Name the device that detects seismic waves. [1]

    ....

    (b) P-waves are seismic waves that travel through the Earth at speeds of 5–8 m/s. What are the main differences between P-waves and S-waves? [3]

    ....

    ....

    ....

    ....

2. The Sun produces ultraviolet waves. Some ultraviolet waves can pass through the atmosphere.

    (a) How is ultraviolet harmful to humans? [1]

    ....

    (b) Ben has sun block with an SPF of 20. What is meant by **SPF**? [1]

    ....

    (c) For how long can Ben stay out safely in the Sun when wearing his sun block?

    Complete the table below. [3]

Safe time in the Sun	
Without sun block	With sun block (SPF 20)
3 minutes	.... minutes
10 minutes	.... minutes
25 minutes	.... minutes

3. Over many years scientists measured the levels of ozone gases in the upper atmosphere. From these measurements they concluded that a hole was developing. In what **two** ways could the scientists ensure their results were reliable? [2]

    ....

    ....

    [Total: .... **/ 11]**

4. The diagram shows P-waves and S-waves through the Earth.

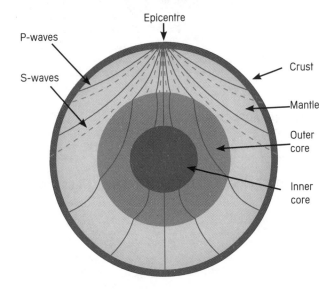

S-waves cannot be detected on the opposite side of the Earth to the epicentre of an earthquake. Describe why S-waves cannot be detected and explain what this tells us about the structure of the Earth. [4]

....

....

....

....

5. Explain the effect that the discovery of the hole in the ozone layer over Antarctica has had on society at an international level. [5]

....

....

....

....

....

[Total: .... **/ 9]**

1. This question is about photocells.

(a) What type of energy do photocells absorb? [1]

....

(b) Photocells can be joined together to form a solar panel. Describe the benefits of doing this. [3]

....

....

....

(c) Give **three other** ways in which the Sun's energy can be harnessed. [3]

....

....

....

2. **(a)** Sarah is a homeowner. What are the **advantages** of attaching electricity-generating photocells to the roof of her house? [3]

....

....

....

(b) What factors should she consider before having photocells fitted? [2]

....

....

3. The UK could generate all of its electricity needs from offshore wind power. What would be the main **advantages** and **disadvantages** of this? [5]

....

....

....

....

....

....

[Total: .... / 17]

---

4. The diagrams show an experiment with a small solar cell.

A   **B**

(a) Explain why the output of the solar cells would differ in positions **A** and **B**.   [2]

....

....

(b) What else could affect the output?   [1]

....

(c) Passive solar heating and a photocell both use the Sun as an energy source. Describe how these two processes differ.   [6]

....

....

....

....

....

....

[Total: .... / 9]

1. **(a)** Describe how to generate electricity using the dynamo effect. [2]

   ....

   ....

   (b) How could the effect be increased? [2]

   ....

   ....

2. Look at the graph below.

   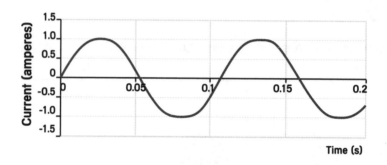

   (a) What kind of current is shown in the graph? Explain your answer. [2]

   ....

   ....

   (b) What devices generate this type of current? .... [1]

3. Electricity can be produced using fossil fuels. Describe the main stages by which electricity
   is produced in a conventional power station. [2]

   ....

   ....

   ....

4. When electricity is produced in a power station some of the energy is wasted as heat. A power station
   uses 12 MW of energy from coal. Only 3 MW of electrical power is produced. Calculate the efficiency
   of the power station. [2]

   ....

   ....

   [Total: .... / 11]

5. The picture shows a power station. As coal is burned in the power station energy is released. The power station wastes 375,000 J of energy as heat in the boiler, turbine, generator and cooling towers.

Overall this power station is 0.25 (25%) efficient. Calculate the total input energy released from the burning coal. [3]

....

....

....

....

[Total: .... / 3]

P2 Global Warming

1. The average surface temperature of the Earth has risen rapidly over the last 100 years.

   Over the last 100 years the levels of solar radiation reaching the Earth have increased. Carbon dioxide concentration in the atmosphere is increasing and one of the factors that is causing this is thought to be increased burning of fossil fuels. Increased carbon dioxide concentration in the atmosphere leads to the greenhouse effect.

   Using the above evidence give an argument that supports man-made global warming and one which refutes it. [4]

2. What does **deforestation** mean and why does it lead to global warming? [3]

3. Give **two** examples of greenhouse gases. [1]

[Total: .... / 8]

Higher Tier

4. Explain how it is possible to have good agreement between scientists about the greenhouse effect but disagreement about whether human activity is affecting global warming. [6]

   ✏ *The quality of your written communication will be assessed in this question.*

5. This graph shows the mean global temperature from 1880 to 2000.

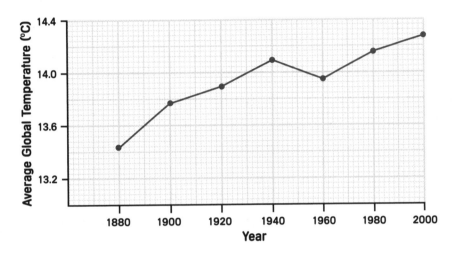

(a) Describe the pattern of global warming shown by the graph. [3]

(b) By how many degrees Celsius did the temperature rise between 1960 and 2000? [1]

[Total: .... / 10]

1. Complete the following table. [6]

Type of fuel used in power stations	Example of fuel	Advantage	Disadvantage
Fossil fuels			
Renewable biomass			
Nuclear fuels			

2. A hairdryer has a current of 10 A through it when plugged into the mains supply (230 V). Calculate the power of the hairdryer. [2]

....

....

3. Electrical appliances use a lot of energy. The energy used by devices such as hairdryers is measured in kWh.

(a) What does the number of kWh of energy used by a device depend on? [1]

....

(b) The lamp shown below uses 4 kWh of energy. Each unit of energy costs 10 pence. Calculate the cost of using this lamp. [2]

....

....

[Total: .... / 11]

4. **(a)** Complete the table below. [4]

Appliance	Power rating in kilowatts	Average time used each week (hours)	Total energy used in a week (kWh)
Hairdryer	2.3	1	
Dishwasher	1.2		3
Washing machine		4	6.8
TV	0.12		1.2

(b) The hairdryer is connected to the 230 V mains. Calculate the current passing through the appliance when it is switched on. [2]

5. Off-peak electricity, like Economy 7, is becoming popular again. Write about the **advantages** and **disadvantages** of off-peak electricity. [4]

Advantages

Disadvantages

6. When a large current is passed through a wire, energy is lost as heat. What are the implications of this for the transmission of power in the national grid? [4]

[Total: .... / 14]

1. Lucy is a radiologist in a hospital. As part of her job she must use radioactive chemicals.

   What precautions should Lucy take when handling radioactive substances? [4]

2. Suggest **one** beneficial use for each of the types of radiation listed below. [3]

   Alpha

   Beta

   Gamma

3. This question is about absorption.

   (a) What material can be used to stop beta? [1]

   (b) Which type of radiation is stopped by a few centimetres of air? [1]

   (c) Which type of radiation is able to pass through concrete? [1]

4. Which type of radiation is the least ionising? [1]

5. When does nuclear radiation form… [2]

   Positive ions

   Negative ions

6. Spent fuel is removed from a nuclear reactor core.

   (a) What element is removed from spent fuel? [1]

(b) Describe how low- and high-level waste is disposed of. [2]

Low-level waste ....

....

High-level waste ....

....

[Total: .... / 16]

Higher Tier

7. The table below shows the results of an experiment investigating the penetration of radiation from three different sources through a selection of different materials (× = radiation detected).

Source	One sheet of paper	Several pieces of thick cardboard	Thin sheet of aluminium	Thick piece of lead
1	×	×		
2	×	×	×	
3				

(a) Identify the radiation produced by sources **1**, **2** and **3**, and explain your choices. [6]

....

....

....

....

....

....

(b) How could the conclusions from this experiment be made more reliable? [1]

....

[Total: .... / 7]

1. Label the following diagrams and number them 1–4 in order of size, starting with the smallest. The first one has already been done for you. [4]

....   Comet   ....

☐   1   ☐   ☐

2. What is a light year? [1]

....

3. (a) The temperature on the surface of Venus is 467°C and its atmosphere consists of carbon dioxide and nitrogen. Would it be better to send a manned spacecraft or an unmanned probe to explore Venus? Explain your answer. [3]

....

....

....

(b) How would the information we got back from Venus be different from information we were able to obtain from the Moon? Explain your answer. [4]

....

....

....

....

4. The Sun is in the centre of our solar system. The eight planets, including Earth, orbit the Sun. In the space below draw Earth's orbit around the Sun. [1]

● Sun

[Total: .... / 13]

Higher Tier

5. What generates the centripetal force that causes the Earth's orbital motion? [2]

....

....

6. A light year is equivalent to 10 trillion kilometres. Describe a suitable situation in the study of space where scientists would use kilometres and a situation when they would use light years. [2]

....

....

....

[Total: .... / 4]

1. Asteroids are large rocks that orbit the Sun.

    (a) What is the difference between an asteroid and a comet? [2]

    ....

    ....

    (b) Scientists believe that asteroids have collided with the Earth in the past. What evidence is there to support this idea? [3]

    ....

    ....

    ....

    (c) Describe how a collision between two planets could lead to the formation of a single planet and a moon. [2]

    ....

    ....

    ....

2. Astronomers use telescopes to observe the trajectories of NEOs.

    (a) What is an NEO? [1]

    ....

    (b) Suggest why scientists need to pay close attention to NEOs. [1]

    ....

    [Total: .... / 9]

Higher Tier

3. Thousands of asteroids orbit the Sun in a large 'belt'. Why don't asteroids join and form new planets? [2]

4. The table below shows a comet's speed at two different distances from the Sun.

Distance from Sun (million km)	Speed of comet (km/s)
5250	0.879
150	54

Explain the above data. [3]

5. What precautions do astronomers take to reduce the risks from NEOs? [3]

6. What evidence is there that the Earth–Moon system is the result of planetary collision? [3]

[Total: _____ / 11]

1. The Big Bang Theory is a theory about how the universe reached its current state.

   (a) What are the **two** main things that this theory tells us about the formation of the universe? [2]

   _____

   _____

   _____

   (b) Explain how observations of space support this theory. [3]

   _____

   _____

   _____

2. All stars begin life as a huge cloud of gas.

   (a) What force causes the gas cloud to collapse and form a star? [1]

   _____

   (b) Which gas do stars initially use? _____ [1]

3. This question is about **heavy-weight** stars. Look at the diagram below. Fill in the missing information. [3]

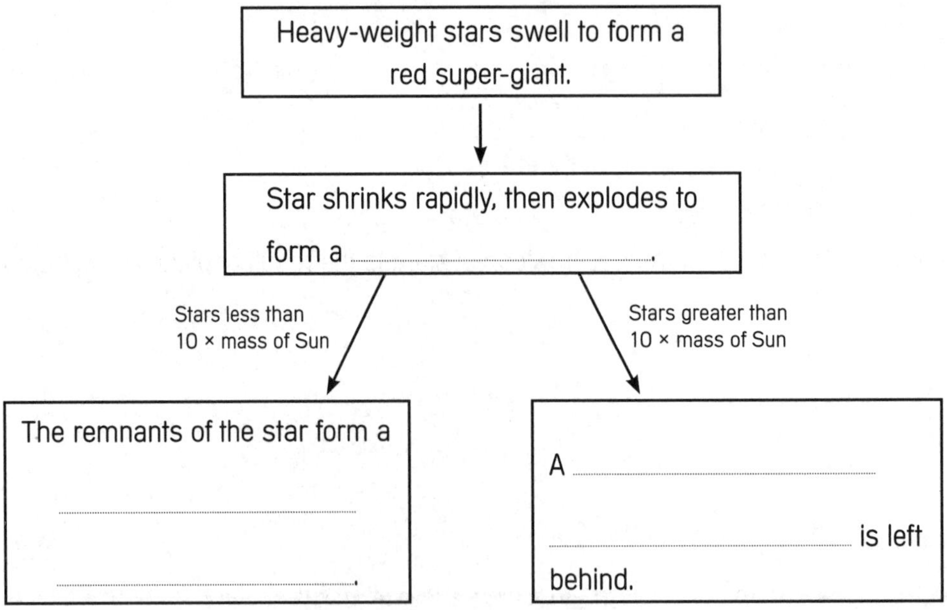

   ┌─────────────────────────────────────┐
   │ Heavy-weight stars swell to form a   │
   │   red super-giant.   │
   └─────────────────────────────────────┘
                      ↓
   ┌─────────────────────────────────────┐
   │ Star shrinks rapidly, then explodes to│
   │ form a _____ .   │
   └─────────────────────────────────────┘

   Stars less than   Stars greater than
   10 × mass of Sun   10 × mass of Sun

   ┌──────────────────────────┐   ┌──────────────────────────┐
   │ The remnants of the star │   │   │
   │ form a   │   │ A _____ │
   │ _____ │   │ _____ is left │
   │ _____ . │   │ behind.   │
   └──────────────────────────┘   └──────────────────────────┘

4. This question is about different models of the universe. Look at the following information comparing the Ptolemaic model and the later Copernican model.

Ptolemaic model	Copernican model
• The Earth was the centre of the universe. • The planets and stars were in fixed positions held in place on crystal spheres.	• The Sun was the centre of the universe. • The planets and stars were in fixed positions in the heavens.

(a) Write down **two** reasons why the Copernican model was not accepted for many years. [2]

....

....

....

(b) Galileo supported much of Copernicus' theory, but he believed that the planets were not in fixed positions. What led him to this assumption? [2]

....

....

....

....

[Total: .... / 14]

Higher Tier

5. 'Red Shift' is evidence that scientists use to support the Big Bang Theory.

(a) What is meant by **red shift**? [2]

....

....

(b) How does the light from galaxies close to us differ from light from very distant galaxies? [2]

....

(c) As well as supporting the Big Bang Theory, what else can scientists use red-shift data to predict? [1]

....

[Total: .... / 5]

Notes

The Periodic Table

Key

| relative atomic mass |
| **atomic symbol** |
| name |
| atomic (proton) number |

1	2											3	4	5	6	7	0
																	4 **He** helium 2
7 **Li** lithium 3	9 **Be** beryllium 4											11 **B** boron 5	12 **C** carbon 6	14 **N** nitrogen 7	16 **O** oxygen 8	19 **F** fluorine 9	20 **Ne** neon 10
23 **Na** sodium 11	24 **Mg** magnesium 12											27 **Al** aluminium 13	28 **Si** silicon 14	31 **P** phosphorus 15	32 **S** sulfur 16	35.5 **Cl** chlorine 17	40 **Ar** argon 18
39 **K** potassium 19	40 **Ca** calcium 20	45 **Sc** scandium 21	48 **Ti** titanium 22	51 **V** vanadium 23	52 **Cr** chromium 24	55 **Mn** manganese 25	56 **Fe** iron 26	59 **Co** cobalt 27	59 **Ni** nickel 28	63.5 **Cu** copper 29	65 **Zn** zinc 30	70 **Ga** gallium 31	73 **Ge** germanium 32	75 **As** arsenic 33	79 **Se** selenium 34	80 **Br** bromine 35	84 **Kr** krypton 36
85 **Rb** rubidium 37	88 **Sr** strontium 38	89 **Y** yttrium 39	91 **Zr** zirconium 40	93 **Nb** niobium 41	96 **Mo** molybdenum 42	[98] **Tc** technetium 43	101 **Ru** ruthenium 44	103 **Rh** rhodium 45	106 **Pd** palladium 46	108 **Ag** silver 47	112 **Cd** cadmium 48	115 **In** indium 49	119 **Sn** tin 50	122 **Sb** antimony 51	128 **Te** tellurium 52	127 **I** iodine 53	131 **Xe** xenon 54
133 **Cs** caesium 55	137 **Ba** barium 56	139 **La*** lanthanum 57	178 **Hf** hafnium 72	181 **Ta** tantalum 73	184 **W** tungsten 74	186 **Re** rhenium 75	190 **Os** osmium 76	192 **Ir** iridium 77	195 **Pt** platinum 78	197 **Au** gold 79	201 **Hg** mercury 80	204 **Tl** thallium 81	207 **Pb** lead 82	209 **Bi** bismuth 83	[209] **Po** polonium 84	[210] **At** astatine 85	[222] **Rn** radon 86
[223] **Fr** francium 87	[226] **Ra** radium 88	[2227] **Ac*** actinium 89	[261] **Rf** rutherfordium 104	[262] **Db** dubnium 105	[266] **Sg** seaborgium 106	[264] **Bh** bohrium 107	[277] **Hs** hassium 108	[268] **Mt** meitnerium 109	[271] **Ds** darmstadtium 110	[272] **Rg** roentgenium 111							

1 **H** hydrogen 1

Elements with atomic numbers 112–116 have been reported but not fully authenticated

*The lanthanoids (atomic numbers 58–71) and the actinoids (atomic numbers 90–103) have been omitted.
The relative atomic masses of copper and chlorine have not been rounded to the nearest whole number.

Equations

Average speed $= \dfrac{\text{Distance}}{\text{Time}}$

Acceleration $= \dfrac{\text{Change in speed}}{\text{Time taken}}$

Force = Mass × Acceleration

Work done = Force × Distance

Distance = Average speed × Time

Power $= \dfrac{\text{Work done}}{\text{Time}}$

$KE = \dfrac{1}{2} mv^2$

Weight = Mass × Gravitational field strength

Force $= \dfrac{\text{Change in momentum}}{\text{Time}}$

Refractive index $= \dfrac{\text{Speed of light in vacuum}}{\text{Speed of light in medium}}$

Power = Force × Speed

Power = Voltage × Current

Energy = Mass × Specific heat capacity × Temperature change

Energy = Mass × Specific latent heat

Efficiency $= \dfrac{\text{Useful energy output (× 100\%)}}{\text{Total energy input}}$

Resistance $= \dfrac{\text{Voltage}}{\text{Current}}$

$v = u + at$

$s = \dfrac{(u + v)}{2} \times t$

Momentum = Mass × Velocity

Magnification $= \dfrac{\text{Image size}}{\text{Object size}}$

$V_p I_p = V_s I_s$

$v^2 = u^2 + 2as$

$s = ut + \dfrac{1}{2} at^2$

$I_e = I_b + I_c$

Wave speed = Frequency x Wavelength

Energy supplied = Power x Time

$GPE = mgh$

$mgh = \dfrac{1}{2} mv^2$

$m_1 u_1 + m_2 u_2 = (m_1 + m_2)v$

Power loss $= (\text{Current})^2 \times$ Resistance

$\dfrac{\text{Voltage across primary coil}}{\text{Voltage across secondary coil}} = \dfrac{\text{Number of primary turns}}{\text{Number of secondary turns}}$

© Lonsdale